DEVELOPING SCIENCE LANGUAGE

for
Living Things
with
10–11
year olds

Neville Evans

Published by Scholastic Ltd,
Villiers House,
Clarendon Avenue,
Leamington Spa,
Warwickshire CV32 5PR
Visit our website at www.scholastic.co.uk

Printed by Alden Group Ltd, Oxford

© 2002 Scholastic Ltd
Text © Neville Evans 2002

1234567890 2345678901

Acknowledgement
The publisher would like to thank David Higham
Associates for the use of an extract from *Naturally Fit*
by Bruce Tulloch © Bruce Tulloch (Arthur Baker Ltd).

The author would like to acknowledge the help
of Kath Phelan as Science Consultant.

AUTHOR
Neville Evans

LITERACY CONSULTANT
Gill Matthews

EDITOR
Joel Lane

ASSISTANT EDITOR
Alison Rosier

SERIES DESIGNER
Rachael Hammond

DESIGNER
Erik Ivens

COVER PHOTOGRAPH
© Stockbyte

ILLUSTRATIONS
Theresa Tibbetts

British Library Cataloguing-in-Publication Data
A catalogue record for this book is available from the British Library.

ISBN 0-439-01878-1

Designed using Adobe Pagemaker

The right of Neville Evans to be identified as the Author of this work
has been asserted by him in accordance with the Copyright, Designs
and Patents Act 1988.

CONTENTS

CONTENTS

INTRODUCTION

Children often struggle to remember science words. Sometimes the words seem strange or unusual, and sometimes the words we use in science have other meanings in everyday life. Think about these science words: *sense, animals, exercises.* If you ask a child what these words mean, you are likely to get responses such as: 'People who talk silly do not make sense'; 'Animals are things with four legs, like cats and dogs'; 'I do my exercises in my green book'. But when children go into science lessons, we sometimes assume that they already understand that 'sense' refers to our five faculties; 'animals' includes birds, fish, insects and humans; and 'exercises' are physical routines to keep our bodies healthy.

Scientific language

This series aims to give children practice in using science words, both through science activities and in 'real life' contexts, so that they become familiar with the meanings of these words. Use of correct scientific vocabulary is essential for high attainment in national assessment tests. The QCA *Scheme of Work for Science* for Key Stages 1 and 2 in England suggests vocabulary for each of its units; although these books are not divided into exactly the same topics, the QCA vocabulary and its progressive introduction are used as the basis for the word selection here.

The science covered is divided into units based on topics from the national curricula for England, Wales, Scotland and Northern Ireland. In this book, the science is drawn from the 'Life processes and living things' statements for ages 8–9 relating to life processes, humans and other animals, green plants, variation and classification and living things in the environment. The boxed letters at the bottom of each page show to which curriculum the focus of each activity relates. For example, for the activity on page 31, the boxes E NI W S indicate that the activity focuses on a topic from the Scottish Guidelines only.

Science literacy

The National Literacy Strategy for England suggests teaching objectives and gives examples of the types of activities that children should encounter during each year of primary school. This book uses many of these techniques for developing children's understanding and use of scientific language. The activities are mainly intended for use in science time, as they have been written with science learning objectives in mind. However, some of the activities could be used in literacy time. Science texts have already been published for use in literacy time, but many of them use science content appropriate for older children.

During literacy time you need to be focusing on language skills, not teaching new science. It is with this in mind that these sheets, drawing from age-appropriate science work, have been produced. It is also suggested that these sheets are used in literacy time only after the science content has been introduced in science time.

The series focuses on paper-based activities to develop scientific language, rather than on experimental and investigative work, but it is hoped that teachers might use some of the ideas in planning practical science activities.

About this book

Each unit in this book begins with a non-fiction text that introduces some key scientific vocabulary. The key words are highlighted by bold type. The texts cover a range of non-fiction genres.

Following this text are two comprehension activities that help children to identify and understand the key words (and a range of additional science words). They are pitched at two levels:

 for older or more able children

 for younger or less able children.

Although the comprehension activities are designed to be used mainly during science time, you may wish to use the texts as examples of non-fiction texts in the literacy hour. The comprehension pages contain two or three types of question:

 The answer can be found in the text.

 Children will need to think about the answer. These questions usually elicit science understanding beyond what the text provides.

 An activity aimed at developing children's literacy skills. These are optional extension activities for individual or group work, with teacher support if necessary.

Following the comprehension pages in each unit are activities aimed at developing children's understanding and use of the key vocabulary. Strategies used include: writing explanations, writing letters, handling data, calculating, explaining, interpreting graphs, planning an investigation, writing instructions, identifying similarities and differences, writing a newspaper report, writing a factfile, interpreting a nursery rhyme, interpreting metaphors, explaining reasons for actions.

WORD LIST

absorb
acid
adapt
addicted
alcohol
alcoholic
alimentary canal
ammonia
anther
antibiotic
aquarium
artery
athlete's foot
attract

bacteria
balanced
beat
bile
biodegradable
blood
blood donor
bloodstream
blood transfusion
blood vessels
boils
brain
breathe
broken down
bubonic plague

calcium
capillary vessels
carbohydrate
carpel
central nervous system
chemicals
chickenpox
circulation
circulatory system
classify
clot
communities
compete
competition
conserve
consumer
consumption
contract
contagious
co-ordinate
cure

decay
diaphragm
diet
digest
digestive system
disease
disperse
dissolve
dormant
drainage
drought
drug

enamel
energy
environment
epidemic
eradicate
excrete
exercise
exhale
extinct

fat
female
ferment
fertile
fertilisation
fertilise
fertiliser
fibre
flowering plant
flower
food chain
food group
food web
fruit
function
fungi

gender
germinate
germ
grow

habitat
harmful
harmony
healthy
heart
herbal
humus

illness
impulse
infect
infectious
influenza
ingest
ingredients
inhale
inoculate
interact
intercostal muscles
iron

key

large intestine
leaf litter
light
liver
lungs

male
medicine
microbe
microscope
minerals
muscle

nerve
nicotine
nutrients

observation
oils
organ
organism
ovary
overcrowding
ovule
oxygen

parasite
pasteurised
petal
pharmacist
photosynthesis
plaque
poison
pollen grains
pollination
polluted
producer

protein
pulse
pulse rate
pump
purify

quarantine

reaction
regenerate
recycle
relax
replenish
reproduce
reproduction
respiration
rib-cage
root
root hair

scent
seed
sexual
shoot
skeleton
small intestine
smoking
soil
species
spinal cord
stamen
sterilised
stigma
stock
survive
symptoms

tar
throat
transmissible

variety
vein
ventilation
vertebrate
virus
vitamins

windpipe

yeast
yoghurt

▪SCHOLASTIC DEVELOPING SCIENCE LANGUAGE for *Living Things* 10–11

Keeping healthy

We all need to eat the correct foods in the correct amounts to remain in good health. Food has three important jobs to do in our bodies; each job is done best by one type of food.

Job 1 is to provide the body with **energy** so that we can be active. This job is done by **carbohydrates** such as sugars and starch. Good sources of carbohydrates include bread, potatoes, rice and pasta. We also get energy from **fats** and **oils**, such as butter and olive oil.

Job 2 is to help build the body so that we grow. This job is done by **proteins**. Good sources of proteins include eggs, fish, meat and beans.

Job 3 is to protect us against illness and **diseases**. This job is done by small amounts of **vitamins** and **minerals**. **Vitamins** are chemicals that are known by letters such as A, B and C. Many **vitamins** occur in fruit and vegetables. Two **minerals** that we need are **iron** for our blood and **calcium** for our bones. These occur in foods in a **dissolved** form. We can get iron from meat and cabbage, and calcium from milk and cheese.

In addition, fruits, vegetables and cereals provide us with **fibre**. This helps us to **digest** food properly so that our bodies get full benefit from it.

If we ate only chips or sugary snacks, we would take in too much carbohydrate and fat but not enough protein, minerals and vitamins. We need a **diet** that is **balanced**: it should contain a **variety** of types of foods, with the right amount of each type.

These are a few hints for good eating habits.
1. Eat only a few sweets.
2. Eat some fresh fruit every day.
3. Eat plenty of vegetables, especially peas and beans.
4. Eat only a small amount of fatty foods such as burgers and chips.
5. Drink only a small amount of sugary drinks such as squash.

Keeping healthy

1. Which three jobs does food do for the body?

a) _____

b) _____

c) _____

2. Which type of food is found in each of these?

a) rice _____   b) fish _____

c) meat _____   d) butter _____

3. Name a particular example of:

A food that gives us energy to be active. _____

A food that helps us to grow. _____

A food that gives us fibre. _____

4. Explain what the words **'balanced diet'** mean.

A balanced diet is _____

_____

_____

5. Explain why it is more important to start each day with a breakfast than to end each day with a dinner or supper.

_____

_____

_____

6. Explain why each day's food should provide us only with the amount of energy that we need for that day.

_____

_____

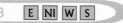 Plan a diet for yourself for one day. Explain why you have chosen these foods.

Keeping healthy

1. What three jobs does food do for our bodies?

a) _____

b) _____

c) _____

2. Which type of food does each of these examples provide?

a) rice _____   b) fish _____

c) meat _____   d) butter _____

3. Write 'True' or 'False' at the end of each sentence.

Proteins give us energy to be active. _____

Fats give us fibre. _____

Fats contain a great deal of energy. _____

4. Explain what the words **'balanced diet'** mean.

A balanced diet is _____

_____

_____

5. If you had to miss a meal, which meal should you not do without: breakfast or dinner? Explain your answer.

_____

_____

_____

6. What would happen if your food every day provided more energy than you needed for that day?

_____

_____

Plan a diet for yourself for one day. Explain why you have chosen these foods.

Daily diet

Fill in the gaps in the text below, using the words in this list.
Use each word once only.

> chemicals   lorry   food   correct   fuel
>
> vehicle   diet   variety   wrong   bodies

A car or lorry or aeroplane cannot move unless we put f_____, such as petrol or diesel, into it. If we put fuel meant for a l_____ into a car, something will go w_____. We must use the c_____ type of fuel for each v_____.

    F_____ is the fuel that we need for our b_____ to work properly. The fuel used in most vehicles is made up of several c_____. One alone won't do the job properly. So it is for us: one type of food alone won't do. We need v_____ in our d_____.

These are the five **food groups** that we need for our daily diet:
Group 1:   bread, cereals, potatoes
Group 2:   fruit, vegetables
Group 3:   milk, dairy foods
Group 4:   meat, fish (or alternatives)
Group 5:   fats and oils

This pie chart shows how much of each food group we should try to eat as a proportion of our daily intake.

Group 1:   at least 5 portions
Group 2:   at least 5 portions
Group 3:   2–3 portions
Group 4:   2–3 portions
Group 5:   0–3 portions

How would the pie chart need to be different for someone who:

●   is getting a lot of exercise every day?

_____

●   is growing quickly as a young teenager?

_____

Food groups

The **food groups** listed on page 10 provide different substances that the body needs: proteins, carbohydrates, fats, vitamins, minerals and fibre.

Complete the table below by writing the names of substances that the body needs and examples of particular foods.

Food group number	Examples of foods	What it provides
1	Bread, rice, pasta, noodles	
2		Fibre and vitamins
3		Minerals
4	Meat, poultry, fish, nuts, beans	
5	Butter, cream, chocolate	

Under each of these pictures, write C, P, Fa, Fi, V or M to indicate whether the food in the picture is a source of carbohydrate (C), protein (P), fat (Fa), fibre (Fi), vitamins (V) or minerals (M). For some foods, you can write more than one letter. For example, beans provide protein (P) and fibre (Fi).

P, Fi

Energy needs

Our food is our fuel. It keeps our bodies warm and healthy. It gives us the **energy** we need to be active.

Different people need different amounts of energy. It depends on their age and level of activity. It also depends on whether they are **male** or **female**. Boys and young men usually need more energy (and so more food) than girls and young women.

Who needs more food (energy): a boy who is 8 years old or a man who is 24 years old? Explain your answer.

_____

_____

_____

We use energy from food even when we are sleeping. Why is this?

_____

This chart shows some typical energy needs for different kinds of people. Use it to answer the questions below.

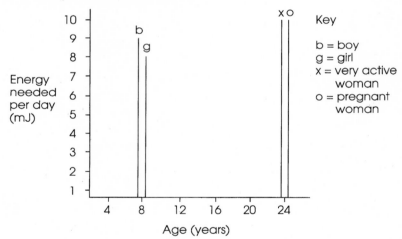

1. About how many units of energy does a girl aged 8 need daily? _____

2. About how many units does a woman aged 24 need daily if she is very active or pregnant? _____

3. Why do you think the energy needs of a very active woman and a pregnant woman are almost the same?

_____

_____

■ S C H O L A S T I C

Keeping fit

In this passage, an Olympic Gold Medallist describes how he trains to improve his **circulation**.

The athlete strengthens his heart by training – it is mostly muscle and responds in the same way, thereby becoming more **efficient**. This can be proved by taking someone's pulse rate before he starts a training programme, and continuing to measure it as training proceeds. Over a period of weeks, it will be found that the rate of the heart beat when the person is at rest gradually decreases. This resting pulse (usually measured immediately after waking in the morning) will be 70 or 80 beats per minute for the average man or woman, but with training it may well drop to 60 or below. My own resting pulse, when completely fit, has been as low as 38. This is because the heart, being stronger than before and capable of pumping more at each beat, does not have to work as hard to keep the body supplied with oxygen.

The other effect of training is to improve the **circulation** to the working muscle, with the result that more **capillary vessels** develop in the muscles that are being used most. These capillaries are not in use when you are at rest; but in an emergency, when more oxygen is needed, they open up to allow more blood to flow. This means that you can 'switch on' to a higher rate of exercise when you really need to. Of course, this would not be any good unless your heart had also strengthened so that it could deal with this extra effort.

(from *Naturally Fit* by Bruce Tulloch, published by Arthur Baker Ltd)

Answer these questions on another sheet of paper.

1. Find out and explain the meaning of the words underlined in the text.

2. As well as the heart, what other organs improve with training? Explain your answer.

3. Describe the changes that might occur in your blood circulation as you become fitter.

A fruit shop

Fruits are an important part of our daily diet. They provide natural sugars, vitamins, minerals and fibre. They do much less damage to our teeth than sugary foods.

Write a plan for setting up a fruit tuck shop in your school. Use the ideas below to help you. When you are answering the questions, use what you know about fruits and why they are important for health.

1.   Who does what job? (This question has been answered for you.)

Selling the fruit	pupils in Year 6
Buying the fruit	all pupils, some teachers

2.   Where shall we put the shop? _____

_____

Why there? _____

3.   Where shall we store the fruit? _____

_____

Why there? _____

4.   When shall we open the shop? _____

_____

Why then? _____

5.   Which fruits shall we sell? _____

_____

Why those fruits? _____

Make a poster to attract people to buy the fruits by explaining why fruits are important for our health.

Nursery rhymes

Many nursery rhymes refer to food, or to animals and plants that we may eat. Your task is to complete this table.

● First write down the names of the foods, or things that we may eat, that occur in each rhyme.
● Then write how these foods can contribute to a healthy diet.

Nursery rhyme	Food	Contribution to diet
The bells of St Clement's	oranges and lemons	vitamins, natural sugars,
Little Jack Horner	plum pie	fibre
Little Miss Muffett		
Georgy Porgy		
Simple Simon		
Queen of Hearts		
Jack and Jill		
To market, to market		
Pat-a-cake		
Hickety, pickety, my black hen		
I had a little nut tree		
Half a pound of tuppenny rice		

Keep it clean

We know that to be healthy we need a diet that is balanced and adequate. We also need sufficient water in our diet.

Of course, we also know is that our food and water must be clean. They must not contain any substances that might harm us.

Shopkeepers have to obey regulations from the local council on how to store the food that they sell.

Write regulations of your own for one particular type of food shop.

1. _____

_____

2. _____

_____

But what about us at home? We do not have to follow the same regulations as shopkeepers, but it is sensible for us to be very careful about how we keep and handle food at home.

What happens to fruit, bread, milk and meat that 'goes off'?

_____

_____

What two things should you do to prevent this happening or slow it down?

1. _____

2. _____

Explain why you should never eat food from a damaged can.

_____

Explain what this proverb means:
One rotten apple can spoil the whole barrel.

_____

Write a letter to the Environmental Services department of your local council, asking what its food regulations are.

Medicines and drugs

If we become ill we may need to take **medicines**. These are **chemicals** that help us to recover from illness by changing the way our bodies work. We should take a medicine only when a doctor or nurse says we need to. If taken at the wrong time or in the wrong amount, medicines can be harmful.

Drugs are substances that change the way our bodies work. Some drugs are medicines, some are not. All drugs can be **harmful**. They can **poison** us or alter the way we behave. Many drugs are **addictive**, which means that it is difficult to stop taking them.

All **alcoholic** drinks contain a chemical called **alcohol**, which slows down our **reactions**. This is very dangerous for vehicle drivers, who may need quick reactions to apply the brakes if a pedestrian steps off the pavement. People who drink a lot of alcohol over a long period of time may become very ill because of damage to **organs** in their bodies, especially the **liver** and the **brain**.

Smoking cigarettes and cigars is also dangerous. Tobacco smoke contains **nicotine**, which is a poisonous, addictive drug. It can damage the **heart**, **blood vessels** and **nerves**. Also, when tobacco smoke cools down it forms **tar**. This is very harmful to the **throat** and **lungs**.

Our bodies need certain chemicals, mostly food and drink, to be healthy. Other chemicals are not good for us, unless we are ill and they will help. Don't put any chemicals into your body unless a doctor, nurse or **pharmacist** approves. Always ask for advice first.

Medicines and drugs

1. Why do we take medicines? _____

_____

2. Why do people use the two words 'medicine' and 'drug'?

_____

_____

3. Describe two ways in which drugs can harm our bodies.

a) _____

b) _____

4. What does it mean to say that someone is an 'addict'?

_____

_____

5. Give three reasons why alcohol is harmful.

a) _____

b) _____

c) _____

6. Which two harmful substances come from tobacco smoke?

a) _____   b) _____

Describe how one of these causes illness. _____

_____

7. Before you take any medicines or drugs, you should get advice. What three kinds of people are the best to advise you?

a) _____   b) _____   c) _____

Write a poster to persuade people not to take drugs, drink alcohol or smoke tobacco because of their harmful effects.

Medicines and drugs

1. Why do we take medicines? _____

_____

2. Cross out the incorrect words in the brackets in this sentence.

Some drugs are (medicines / chemicals), but all drugs can be (useful / harmful).

3. Describe two ways in which drugs can harm our bodies.

a) _____

b) _____

4. Write 'True' or 'False' after this sentence.

Addictive drugs are difficult to give up. _____

5. Write three reasons why alcohol is harmful.

a) _____

b) _____

c) _____

6. Cross out the chemicals that are not in tobacco smoke.

| oxygen | tar | nicotine | copper |

7. Before you take any medicines or drugs, you should get advice. Who are the best people to advise you?

a) _____   b) _____   c) _____

Write a poster to persuade people not to take drugs, drink alcohol or smoke tobacco because of their harmful effects.

Acrostic poems

What is an acrostic poem? _____

_____

_____

Here is an acrostic poem about drugs.

Danger! Danger! Senses dulled.
Rambling speech reveals no
Understanding of what
Ghastly consequences flow from what
Seemed like simple fun.

Write your own acrostic poem about drugs. Emphasise their dangers. Note your ideas in the box before writing your poem.

D _____

R _____

U _____

G _____

S _____

Now write an acrostic poem using the word MEDICINES. Emphasise their benefits. Note your ideas on the back of this sheet before writing your poem on another sheet.

■ SCHOLASTIC

Don't smoke

Many doctors in a number of countries have kept records of the health of smokers and non-smokers. They agree that smoking damages health. The tobacco smoke that is **inhaled** is harmful to the mouth, **windpipe**, lungs and heart. Damage to the lungs means that not enough oxygen gets into the **bloodstream**. Damage to the heart means that the blood is not pumped around the body as quickly as it should be. Because they do not get enough oxygen from their blood supply, other organs of the body work less well.

Name the product in tobacco smoke that damages:

a) the lungs _____ b) the heart _____

Do the lungs recover while a smoker is sleeping? Explain your answer.

_____

_____

A person's feet are not directly affected by tobacco smoke. Why might they be harmed by smoking? Think about long-term changes in the body.

_____

_____

This graph shows some information from a survey in Britain of serious heart disease and smoking in men between 45 and 54 years of age. Answer these questions on another sheet of paper.

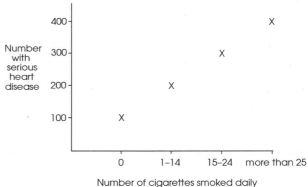

Number of cigarettes smoked daily

1. Among the people who smoked 1–14 cigarettes daily, how many had serious heart disease?

2. How many of those who smoked more than 25 cigarettes daily had serious heart disease?

3. Does this chart prove that smoking is the ONLY cause of heart disease? Explain your answer.

Alcohol

Answer 'Yes' or 'No' to each question.

Are fruits good for our health? _____

Are vegetables good for our health? _____

Are cereal foods such as grain good for our health? _____

The answer to each question is the same. Yet these three beneficial ingredients can all be used to make a chemical that can be very harmful to us. The chemical is known as alcohol.

Alcoholic drinks are made by **fermenting** fruit, vegetables or grain. The sugar or starch in these foods is changed to alcohol by the action of yeast. Alcohol is an ingredient of many drinks, such as beer, lager, wine, whisky and sherry. If misused, these drinks can all be very dangerous.

Use what you know to answer these questions.

> How is too much alcohol harmful to the drinker's body?

1. _____

2. _____

3. _____

> How can one person drinking too much cause harm to others?

1. _____

2. _____

3. _____

Herbal medicine

For a very long time in the past, people used plants to make their own **herbal** medicines for **curing** illnesses. This still happens today, though we now have many medicines that are made in factories.

Camomile flowers can be made into a drink that people take to ease an upset stomach.

Agrimony, which has small yellow flowers, can be used to heal wounds.

Find out about some plants that are used as medicines. You may need to visit a herbalist's shop or write to someone for information. This list of plants may help you to start:

peppermint   dock   aloe   dandelion   rose hip   elderflower

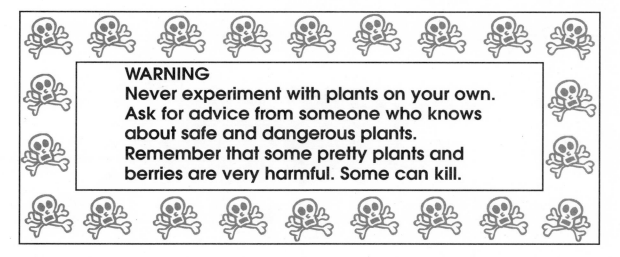

WARNING
Never experiment with plants on your own.
Ask for advice from someone who knows
about safe and dangerous plants.
Remember that some pretty plants and
berries are very harmful. Some can kill.

Use what you have found out to write a short report for a newspaper about herbal medicine.

Some plants are poisonous, and people should avoid touching or eating them. Find out about these three plants. Make notes on where they grow and what they look like. Use your notes to make a warning notice called 'Plants to avoid'.

1. Deadly nightshade (Belladonna)
2. Foxglove
3. Laburnum

What a pain!

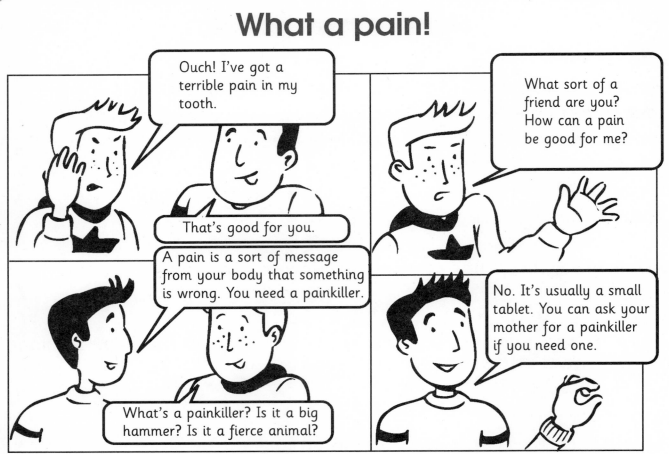

1. Is Samir giving Ben good advice about what pain is? Write and explain your answer on another sheet.

2. What advice would you offer Ben now?

3. Find out about medicines that help us to cope with aches and pains. Write some notes, then write and illustrate a notice telling people when and how to use painkillers. Remember to include appropriate warnings.

4. Do you think taking a pill is a 'sure cure' for a problem of this kind? Explain your answer.

The body machine

Inside our bodies, under the skin, are many different parts that are associated with each other in various ways. A part of the body that has a particular job to do is called an **organ**. When its organs are working together in **harmony**, the body is healthy.

Our bodies cannot make their own food. They have to take in food and water. In order for the body to make use of it, food has to be **digested**. This means that it is **broken down** into much smaller parts and the useful chemicals are **absorbed**. To make this happen, the body has several organs that work together as the **digestive system**.

Digestive system

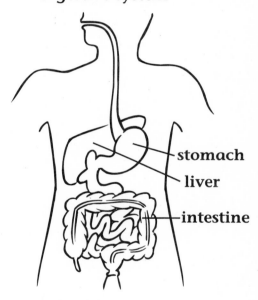

- stomach
- liver
- intestine

Our bodies also need to take in **oxygen** from the air, which is why we **breathe**. Inside the body, the oxygen is used to release **energy** from food. The body needs this energy to be active, to grow and to **regenerate** or heal.

The oxygen that we **inhale** (breathe in) goes directly to our **lungs.** From there, it is **absorbed** into the **blood**, which is pumped by the **heart** through a system of channels (**blood vessels**) so that the oxygen reaches the rest of the body. This system is called the **circulatory system**.

Circulatory system

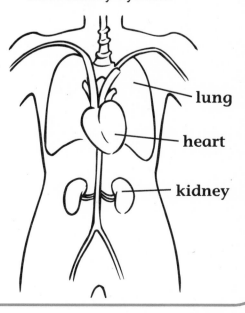

- lung
- heart
- kidney

These diagrams show the **internal** organs of the body in the two systems for circulation and digestion.

The body machine

1. What is the name of the body system that deals with food and drink?

_____

2. What happens to food in our bodies so that we can make use of it?

It is _____. This means _____

_____

3. Why do we need to breathe? _____

_____

What job does oxygen do in the body? _____

_____

4. What substance is carried around
the body in the circulatory system? _____

Which organ pumps this substance around the body? _____

5. Find out which part of the skeleton plays
an important part in helping us to breathe. _____

How does it help us to breathe? _____

_____

6. What simple method can you use
to measure how your heart is working? _____

This method will give you a number that will be different for people of
different ages. Find out the approximate values you would expect for a
healthy baby and a healthy teenager.

_____ and _____

Find out about what your stomach does. Write a short report about the job
that it does.

The body machine

1. Something needs to happen to our food if it is to be useful to us. Underline the name of the process that happens to food.

> digestion   digression   depression   dissection

2. During this process, what happens to the useful chemicals in our food? Tick the correct answer.

They are absolved. ☐   They are absorbed. ☐   They are abstracted. ☐

The answer I have ticked means that the chemicals _____

_____

3. Why do we need to breathe? _____

_____

What important job does oxygen do in the body? _____

_____

4. What substance is carried around the body in the circulation system? _____

5. Find out which part of the skeleton plays an important part in helping us to breathe. _____

How does it help us to breathe? _____

_____

6. Write the correct word in each gap in this sentence.

My _____ pumps blood around my body. I can tell how

fast my heart is beating by measuring my _____ at my wrist.

Look in books to find out the approximate values for:
● how fast a baby's heart beats
● how fast a teenager's heart beats.

Find out about what your stomach does. What system is it part of? What does it take in? Write a short report about the job your stomach does.

Why we breathe

Everything our bodies do requires energy, which is locked inside the food and drink that we **ingest**. This is the science word for 'take in through the mouth'.

The energy in food and drink has to be set free before we can use it to do various jobs (**functions**) in our bodies. The process for releasing energy is called **respiration**. It normally requires **oxygen**.

We obtain oxygen from the air, which we breathe in with our **lungs**. Most people have two lungs, one on each side of the chest. It is possible to live quite healthily with only one lung, as many people do after a lung has been removed because of illness.

The movement of air into and out of the lungs is called **ventilation**. Inside the lungs, oxygen from the air passes through the walls of the lungs into the blood, which then carries it to all parts of the body.

How does ventilation of the lungs happen? Look at the diagrams on the opposite page. Use books to find the meanings of **diaphragm** and **intercostal muscles**.

Now write captions below the diagrams to explain what is happening when we **inhale** (breathe in) and **exhale** (breathe out).

Breathing in and out

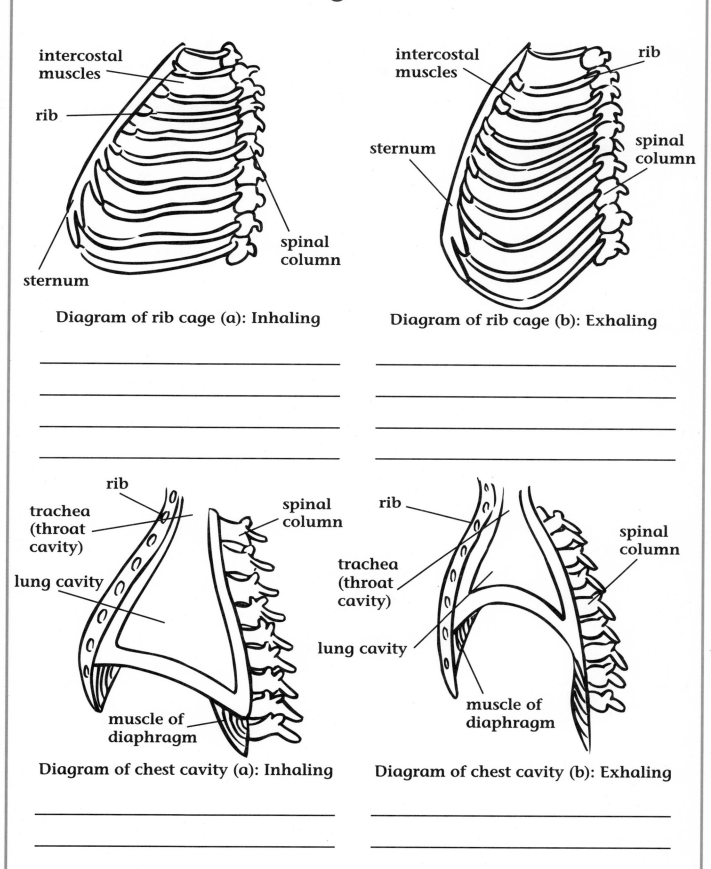

intercostal
muscles

rib

sternum

spinal
column

Diagram of rib cage (a): Inhaling

_____
_____
_____
_____

intercostal
muscles

rib

sternum

spinal
column

Diagram of rib cage (b): Exhaling

_____
_____
_____
_____

rib

trachea
(throat
cavity)

lung cavity

spinal
column

muscle of
diaphragm

Diagram of chest cavity (a): Inhaling

_____
_____
_____
_____

rib

trachea
(throat
cavity)

lung cavity

spinal
column

muscle of
diaphragm

Diagram of chest cavity (b): Exhaling

_____
_____
_____
_____

A model of the lungs

These drawings show you how to make a moving model of the human lungs and diaphragm.

●   Underneath the drawings are the instructions for making the model. These instructions have been mixed up. Cut out the pictures and instructions. On another sheet, stick each instruction under the correct picture.

●   Now make the model.

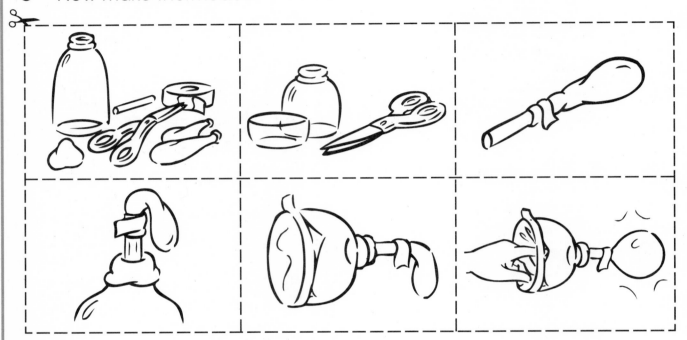

Cut open the large balloon and stretch it over the bottom of the bottle. Fasten it in place with sticky tape. This represents the diaphragm.	You will need: a plastic bottle, a small balloon, a larger balloon, an empty pen barrel, some modelling clay, scissors, sticky tape.	Pinch the skin of the larger balloon between finger and thumb, then push it in and pull it out gently so that the smaller balloon inflates and deflates.
Fasten the pen barrel in the neck of the bottle with clay.	Attach the small balloon to one end of the pen barrel with sticky tape. This represents the windpipe and a lung.	Cut the bottom off the plastic bottle. The bottle represents the chest.

Use this model to explain to your teacher how we breathe in and out. You can make notes to help you explain if you want.

The human liver

The **liver** is an important organ in the human body. It is below the diaphragm, close to the stomach on the right side of the body. Other vertebrates also have livers.

The liver is a kind of regulating, cleaning and storing depot for liquids in the body, especially the blood. This list shows some of the things that the liver does.

1. It regulates the amount of sugar (glucose) in the blood by storing it and releasing it when needed.

2. It produces **bile**, which helps us to digest (break down) fats in our food.

3. It protects us against a chemical called **ammonia**, which can be released from foods and is very poisonous to our body cells.

4. It stores **iron** from red blood cells that have worn out.

5. It makes **proteins** that the blood needs in order to **clot**.

6. It cleans up the blood by getting rid of poisonous substances. Some of these are converted to harmless substances that can be **excreted** in the urine. One such poisonous substance is alcohol. It takes the liver about three hours to clean up after one pint of beer. Some heavy drinkers suffer from liver failure.

7. It stores two important vitamins, A and D. This is why animal livers are a healthy ingredient for our diet.

8. It generates heat by its activity, and so helps to keep up the body's temperature.

Answer these questions on another sheet of paper.

1. a) If a person drinks five pints of beer on five nights every week, how many hours in each week will that person's liver have to work to 'clean up' the blood?

b) How does this help to explain why people who drink a lot of alcohol sometimes suffer from liver failure?

2. a) What happens when blood 'clots'?

b) Why is this important for keeping us well?

3. What might happen to a person whose diet is deficient in vitamin A and vitamin D? You will need to find the answer in a science book.

Make a poster to tell people how important the liver is.

How large is a lung?

How large is a person's lung? We cannot answer this question without other information. What other information do we need?

Think of a cartoon character's body. Imagine that its lungs are shaped like boxes inside the chest.

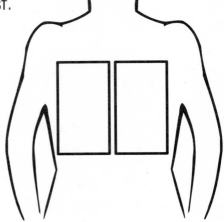

Let's think of just one box (lung) and make the figures easy.

    Estimate of length (down the chest) = 30cm
    Estimate of width (across the chest) = 30cm
    Estimate of depth (into the chest) = 20cm

What is the volume of one of the boxes (lungs)?

    Volume = length × width × depth

           = 30 × 30 × 20 cubic cm

           = _____ cubic cm

How useful is this figure? Remember that oxygen passes through the walls of the lung. So a more useful figure for the 'size' would be the total area of the inside surfaces of the box.

How many internal surfaces does the box have? _____

    Area of front and back surfaces = 2 × 30 × 30 = _____cm^2

    Area of left and right side surfaces = 2 × 30 × 20 = _____cm^2

    Area of top and bottom surfaces = 2 × 30 × 20 = _____cm^2

    Total internal surface area = 4200cm^2

However, this is not a large enough surface area for sufficient oxygen to get through for the body's needs. Scientists estimate that a surface area of about 900,000cm^2 is needed. This is about 200 times as much.

How does the body manage this? Look at the diagrams on the opposite page and write an explanation on another sheet.

Try the paper folding exercise on the opposite page.

Repeat the calculations above, using measurements of your own chest size.

How large is a lung? (2)

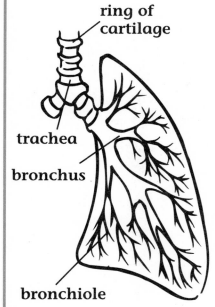

ring of cartilage

trachea

bronchus

bronchiole

1. Air passages in the lungs

bronchiole

alveolus

2. Alveoli in the lungs

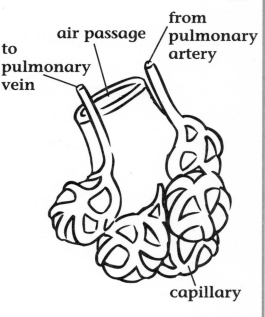

to pulmonary vein

air passage

from pulmonary artery

capillary

3. Blood supply of an alveolus

Folding and surface area

1. Take a sheet of A4 paper. Measure its length (l) and its width (w) in cm.

2. Calculate its area:

$l \times w =$ _____

3. Starting from the top, draw horizontal lines across the page, 1.5cm apart (see illustration on right). Carry on until you reach the bottom.

4. Fold the paper along the lines in a zig-zag pattern, like this:

5. What is the length of the folded-up sheet of paper? _____

6. What is its area? _____

This activity shows how a large area can be fitted into a much smaller space by folding or creasing it. Think about how this fact is important for our lungs.

Systems of the body

The **brain** is the organ that controls all of the life processes in the body. All movements of muscles and systems to maintain the circulation of blood are governed by messages from the brain. These messages (or **impulses**) are electrical and are carried along the **nerves**. The brain is connected to the **spinal cord** which is a sort of main 'highway' for messages. The brain and spinal cord are called the **central nervous system**.

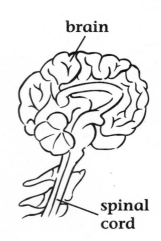

brain

spinal cord

When we run, the brain **co-ordinates** messages to provide blood (carrying sugar and oxygen) more quickly for the leg muscles. If we touch something very hot a message goes to the brain, which sends a message to the arm muscles to move the hand away from the heat.

Another system in the body that has a main route is the digestive system. The main route in this case is called the **alimentary canal**. Its walls are soft and flexible, continually pushing food along and helping to break it up.

mouth
oesophagus
liver
stomach
large intestine
small intestine
rectum

At different points along this canal, food is processed to extract the substances that the body needs. The **small intestine** absorbs almost all of the digested food in the form of substances that pass into the blood. The **large intestine** absorbs most of the water from the undigested food, and pushes most of the solid matter out of the body as waste.

1. Write an explanation for a science magazine of how the central nervous system is like a telephone exchange. Use the vocabulary: wires, switchboard, messages.

2. Write another explanation of how the digestive system is like a system of canals for transporting goods from one place to another. Use the vocabulary: locks, unloading, cargo.

Heart and blood

One way for us to stay healthy is to **exercise** regularly. This keeps our **muscles** in good condition.

During exercise, we usually feel hot and tired. This is because our muscles are working hard and need more **oxygen**. Muscles need oxygen to release energy from food. To take in more oxygen, we breathe more quickly. To carry the oxygen faster from our lungs to our muscles, our **blood** must flow faster – so the **heart** needs to beat faster. We know the heart beats faster during exercise, because our **pulse rate** goes up.

With this extra energy, the muscles are able to move parts of the skeleton, so that we can run, walk, swim and be active in other ways.

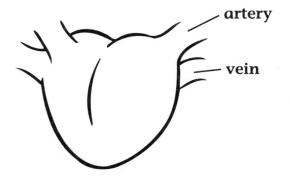

artery

vein

The heart is to the left of the centre of the chest. It is protected by the **rib cage**. The heart is a **pump**. Muscles in the walls of the heart **contract** and **relax** to pump blood around the entire body.

Blood flows away from the heart in **blood vessels** (a system of tubes) called **arteries**. Blood flows back to the heart in vessels called **veins**.

The heart has to work very hard all the time, even when we are resting. We need to look after our hearts as well as we can. Here are some ways to do this:
- Do exercises regularly and often.
- Do not smoke.
- Eat only a little fat, but plenty of fruit.
- Avoid becoming overweight.

Heart and blood

1. Why does your heart beat faster during exercise?

_____

2. What two effects do you usually feel during exercise?

a) _____

b) _____

3. What do your muscles need in order to do work?

_____

4. Why do your breathing rate and your pulse rate slow down during a rest after exercise? _____

_____

5. Which blood vessels carry blood to the heart? _____
Which blood vessels carry blood away from the heart? _____

6. Describe three ways to look after your heart.

a) _____

b) _____

c) _____

7. Explain why the heart is necessary.

_____

_____

Ask your teacher for a copy of the human body outline sheet. Write the letter X to show where the heart is. Use a red pen or pencil to show the flow of blood from the heart to the left leg. Use a blue pen or pencil to show the flow of blood from the right arm to the heart. Label your diagram with the words 'heart', 'vein' and 'artery'.

Note for teacher: a resource page to support the extension task is provided on page 38. It might be helpful to enlarge this page to A3 size.

Heart and blood

1. Why does your heart beat faster when you run?

_____

2. What two effects do you feel during exercise?

a) _____

b) _____

3. Cross out the incorrect words in the brackets in this sentence:

Muscles need (oxygen / air) to move parts of the (skeleton / nerve).

4. Write 'True' or 'False' after this sentence:

When I rest after exercise, my pulse rate slows down. _____

5. Which blood vessels carry blood to the heart? _____

Which blood vessels carry blood away from the heart? _____

6. Describe three ways to look after your heart.

a) _____

b) _____

c) _____

7. What would happen to our blood if we did not have a heart?

_____

_____

Ask your teacher for a copy of the human body outline sheet. Write the letter X to show where the heart is. Use a red pen or pencil to show the path of blood from the heart to the left leg. Use a blue pen or pencil to show the path of blood from the right arm to the heart. Label your diagram with the words 'heart', 'vein' and 'artery'.

Note for teacher: a resource page to support the extension task is provided on page 38. It might be helpful to enlarge this page to A3 size.

Human body outline

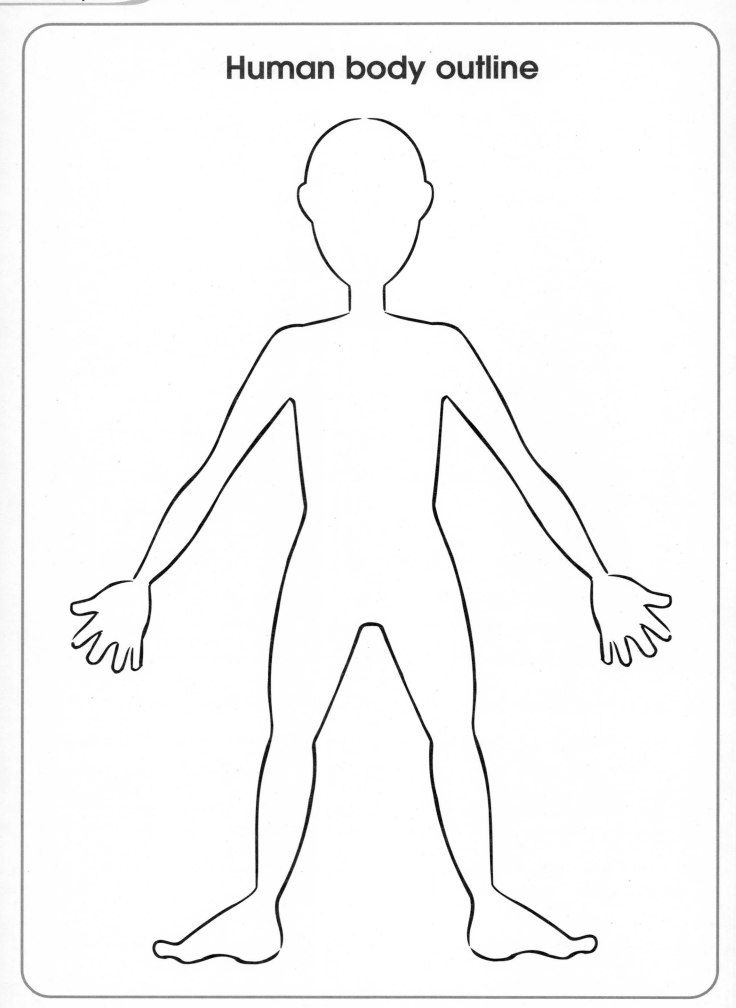

DEVELOPING SCIENCE LANGUAGE for Living Things 10–11

A pump for the blood

The heart is often described as a 'pump'. How does your dictionary define a pump? _____

_____

We can move some water from one tank to another by placing a water pump in the pipe between the two tanks.

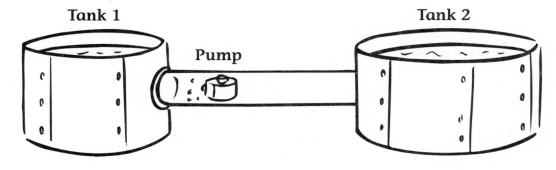

Now think about the heart and what it does.

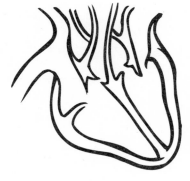

Is your heart like the water pump?

Describe two ways in which they are similar.

1. _____

_____

2. _____

_____

Describe two ways in which they are different.

1. _____

_____

2. _____

_____

Blood vessels

This is a simple diagram of the blood circulation in the body.

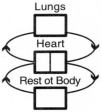

The curved lines on the diagram show the main blood vessels. What do the arrows show? _____

Write the word 'artery' or 'vein' next to each curved line to show which type of blood vessel it is.

Why is there a line down the middle of the block that shows the heart?

_____

The blood vessels shown on the left-hand side of the diagram carry blood that is different from the blood on the other side. What is the difference?

_____

_____

What organ of the body makes this difference? _____

Why is it necessary for the blood to go round in these two different 'circulations'? _____

_____

_____

Which statement do you agree with? Explain.

_____

_____

_____

Blood flow

The heart is a muscle. It pumps blood because it contracts (gets smaller) and then relaxes. It goes through this cycle regularly if it is healthy.

Approximately how many times in every minute does this cycle occur? _____

Remember that this pulse rate can be different for different people, even when they are all healthy. Do not be worried if yours is different. Speak to an adult if you want to know more.

Approximately how many litres of blood are there in the human body? _____

Blood flows through the heart at the rate of about 5 litres per minute. Approximately how long do you think it takes a drop of blood to go from one side of the heart right around the body and back to the same side of the heart? _____

This diagram shows a system of pipes in which water is flowing. All the pipes are full and no water leaks out. The diameter of the pipes is different in different places.

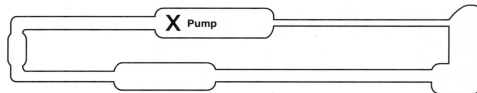

What can you say about the speed of water flow in different parts of this

system of pipes? _____

Our circulatory system is like this. What can you say about the speed of

blood flow in our bodies? _____

If the speed of blood flow in the arteries and veins is different, how do you think the blood gets back to the heart? Tick the two correct answers.

There are more veins than arteries. ☐

The blood moves by itself. ☐

The muscles in our arms and legs help. ☐

Investigating the heart

Look in a science textbook to find the meaning of the word 'physiology'.

Physiology is _____

_____

An aspect of human physiology that people have been thinking about for a long time is how the heart works and how blood circulates.

Among the earliest ideas came from a Roman doctor called Galen. He lived about 2000 years ago. He thought that the heart was like a lamp or a furnace where the blood was made pure. Galen's theories were based on observation of living people.

After Galen, about 1500 years passed before the idea was formed that the heart is a kind of pump that propels blood around the body. The scientist who developed this idea was William Harvey (1578–1657). The pump model is still the basis of our understanding of the heart today.

Harvey investigated the heart by cutting apart the bodies of dead animals, and sometimes even living ones. He studied hard to try to understand the heart, but it was not easy. This is part of what he wrote after looking inside the chest at the rapid heartbeat of a living mammal.

'I kept finding the matter so truly hard, so beset with difficulties... I could not rightly distinguish... when or where constriction and dilation occurred. This was because of the rapidity of the movement... My mind was all at sea...'

1. Look in books to find out more about Galen and his ideas. Why were these ideas believed for so long after Galen?

2. Write the meanings of the words 'constriction', 'dilation' and 'rapidity'.

3. Read about William Harvey and write a factfile about his work. These questions may help you:
- Where did he work?
- How did he investigate the heart?
- What did he find out?
- How was his discovery useful?

The pulse rate

Your pulse rate gives a measure of how fast your heart is beating.

What does 'pulse' mean? _____

_____

What does 'rate' mean? _____

_____

How do you take your pulse? Write words and/or draw a picture to explain.

We know that the heart beats faster during exercise.

Two children, Ranjit and Anna, investigated how their pulse rates were changed by 5 minutes of exercise. Here are their results.

Minutes after starting exercise	1	2	3	4	5	6	7	8	9	10
Number of pulses – Ranjit	80	162	161	159	160	154	135	96	87	82
Number of pulses – Anna	79	90	151	150	152	137	127	100	90	85

1. Draw a graph to show these results on a sheet of graph paper. Remember to label your graph correctly. Answer the following questions on the back of your graph paper, or on another sheet.

2. For both children's pulse rates, describe what happened:
● in the first 2 minutes of exercise
● in the next 3 minutes of exercise
● in the 5 minutes after exercise stopped.

3. Write an explanation of these results.

4. What do you think happened to the pulse rates after 10 minutes of the experiment?

5. Compare the results for Ranjit and for Anna. Describe two differences between the two children's results.

A blood transfusion

Read this story, then answer the questions.

Dr Higgins examined a patient's blood sample under the microscope. This patient didn't have enough **white cells** in his blood to fight off the infection that was making him ill.

He paused as Nurse Wilson ran into the laboratory. 'Doctor!' she cried. 'We have a patient who's been in an accident. He needs a **blood transfusion** urgently. But we're out of type AB negative. It's a rare **blood group** in this part of the country. What can we do?'

Dr Higgins smiled. 'Don't worry,' he said. 'There's a suitable **blood donor** in this hospital. In fact, you're talking to him.' He rolled back his sleeve. 'There's no time to lose.'

The nurse took half a litre of Dr Higgins' blood. 'I can spare that much,' he thought. 'I have six litres of blood in my **circulation**, and my body will replace the missing amount of blood within a day. But a patient  who's lost blood in an accident needs to restore the blood volume urgently. A transfusion is the only answer.'

1. Make a list of all the words in bold in this story. Write a short explanation of what each word or phrase means.

2. Find out about the work of the National Blood Transfusion Service in your area. Write a short report. Include the answers to these questions:
- What happens in a blood donation session?
- Where are the donation sessions held?
- How often can a donor donate blood?
- How many people gave blood in the last session?

Microbes and disease

Microbes are tiny **organisms** that can only be seen through a **microscope**. They exist almost everywhere on Earth. They need food and water to **grow** and **reproduce**. They can **survive** in extreme conditions where most larger organisms would die – and then, in better conditions, they can reproduce very fast. This is why they can be dangerous.

Microbes that cause **diseases** or **illnesses** are often called **germs**. They affect most plants and animals. There are several types of microbes, including **fungi**, **viruses** and **bacteria**.
- **Fungi** cause bread and other foods to go mouldy. **Athlete's foot** is caused by a fungus growing between the toes.
- **Viruses** cause human diseases such as colds, **influenza** and **chickenpox**.
- **Bacteria** cause spots and **blood poisoning**. Bacteria also change **plaque** on our teeth into **acid**, which attacks the **enamel** surfaces. This is why it is important to brush our teeth regularly and often in order to reduce tooth **decay**.

Several famous scientists have studied the microbes that cause diseases. Louis Pasteur discovered that microbes from the air enter food and drink to make them 'go off' or spoil, so that they are unfit for human **consumption**. Joseph Lister realised that people can die from blood poisoning if their wounds become **infected** by bacteria.

These days, we know that microbes can be controlled in three ways:
- by killing them (with heat or chemicals)
- by preventing them getting to places where they can do harm
- by preventing them from growing (with cold).

Under different kinds of **microscope**, microbes look like this:

bacterium   virus   fungus

Microbes and disease

1. What do these words mean?

Microbe: _____

Germ: _____

2. Write the names of three types of microbes.

a) _____ b) _____ c) _____

3. What do microbes need to grow and reproduce?

_____ and _____

4. Draw a line to connect each disease to the type of microbe that causes it.

influenza	**virus**
athlete's foot	
chicken-pox	**bacteria**
spots	
colds	**fungus**
tooth decay	

5. Explain why brushing your teeth often and regularly is important.

_____

6. Describe two ways in which we can control microbes.

a) _____

b) _____

7. Why is it so difficult to get rid of microbes?

_____

_____

8. Why do you think one type of milk we drink is called **pasteurised**?

_____

Use books and CD-ROMs to find out more about Louis Pasteur or Joseph Lister. Now imagine that you are living at the same time as one of these scientists. Write a letter to a friend describing the new discovery and explaining how it may change life in the future.

Microbes and disease

1. Write 'True' or 'False' after each sentence.

A microbe cannot be seen through a microscope. _____

Germs are microbes that cause disease. _____

2. Write the names of three types of microbes.

a) _____ b) _____ c) _____

3. What do microbes need in order to grow and reproduce?

_____ and _____

4. Draw a line to connect each disease to the type of microbe that causes it.

influenza	**virus**
athlete's foot	
chicken-pox	**bacteria**
spots	
colds	**fungus**
tooth decay	

5. Cross out the incorrect words in brackets in these sentences.
(Viruses / bacteria) cause tooth decay by changing (plaque / enamel) on our teeth into (sugar / acid). Tooth decay (can / cannot) be reduced by regular and frequent brushing.

6. Write two ways in which we can control microbes.

a) _____

b) _____

7. Why is it very difficult to get rid of microbes? Tick the best answer.

They are small.   They are quiet.   They can survive in extreme conditions.

8. One type of milk that we drink is called **pasteurised**. Why do you think it has this name? Think of a famous scientist.

_____

Use books and CD-ROMs to find out more about Louis Pasteur or Joseph Lister. Now imagine that you are living at the same time as one of these scientists. Write a letter to a friend describing the new discovery. Explain why the discovery is useful and how it may change things in the future.

Parasites

This is a poem
by DH Lawrence.

The Mosquito Knows
The mosquito knows full well, small as he is
he's a beast of prey.
But after all
he only takes his bellyful
he doesn't put my blood in the bank.

What is a 'beast of prey'? _____

_____

The second part of the poem advises us (humans) to follow the example of the mosquito. What advice is the poet giving us? Think about being greedy.

_____

Read the following passage. Look in books to find out what the underlined words mean. On another sheet of paper, write a **glossary** with these words listed in alphabetical order and followed by their definitions.

Malaria is a **fever** that affects many millions of people, especially in **tropical** countries. It is often **fatal**.

It is caused by a **parasite** – a **microbe** called *Plasmodium*, which is transferred to a person's **bloodstream** when an **infected** mosquito sucks blood from the person. The mosquito lives on animal blood.

Once it is in the human bloodstream, the parasite attacks **red blood cells** and can reproduce in large numbers. If it invades the **liver**, the **host** can become extremely ill.

It is not easy for people to avoid being bitten by the mosquito because it is so small and it moves so fast. People are more exposed when they undress at night. Sometimes they protect themselves by draping mosquito nets over their beds.

People who travel to tropical countries on business or holidays are advised to have an **injection** of drugs to strengthen their body defences against the parasite.

Malaria can strike a person many years after he or she was bitten. This is because the parasite can lie **dormant** in the body and then suddenly become active.

Diseases wordsearch

Find these **diseases** in the wordsearch below. The words can be read horizontally, vertically or diagonally, and either forward or backwards.

chickenpox	mumps	malaria	tetanus
smallpox	impetigo	diphtheria	polio
cholera	tuberculosis	rubella	measles

S	X	O	P	L	L	A	M	S	T	N	T
O	G	I	T	E	P	M	I	F	U	R	E
A	J	D	L	M	W	A	I	L	B	G	T
I	R	A	T	U	C	H	O	L	E	R	A
R	S	N	U	M	F	K	I	N	R	U	N
E	M	I	S	P	O	L	I	O	C	N	U
H	A	E	W	S	C	A	T	S	U	D	S
H	L	L	A	S	R	U	B	E	L	L	A
T	A	N	D	S	N	I	F	F	O	X	Y
P	R	I	C	E	L	I	T	L	S	N	V
I	I	X	O	P	N	E	K	C	I	H	C
D	A	H	E	M	U	L	S	E	S	N	X

Fill in this table to show what causes each of the diseases.

Caused by bacteria	Caused by a virus

Find out more about one of the diseases. Write a report. Your report should try to answer these questions.

- What are its symptoms?
- Where and when was it (or is it) prevalent?
- Has it been generally **eradicated** by now?
- Is there a **cure** for this disease? If so, what is it?
- If not, how has the disease been prevented?

Transmission of diseases

Many diseases or illnesses can be spread from sick people to healthy people. These diseases are often described as **transmissible,** which means that they can be passed on. Two other words that are used to describe diseases are '**infectious**' and '**contagious**'.

● **Contagious** diseases can only be passed on if there is physical contact between people, or contact with the clothes or bed linen of sick people. Examples of contagious diseases include tinea (ringworm) and athlete's foot.

● **Infectious** diseases can be passed on without contact – for example, through air or water. Examples of infectious diseases include tuberculosis, chickenpox, measles, whooping cough and influenza.

Diseases can be spread and prevented in several ways. Find out and write about the three diseases named in the table below. Use the table to make notes, then write a report. The following words may be useful to you:

| hygiene | quarantine | drainage | inoculation |

Name of disease	How it can be spread	How it can be prevented
Common cold		
Measles		
Food poisoning (Salmonella bacteria)		

Bubonic plague

A well-known nursery
rhyme runs as follows:

Ring-a-ring o' roses,
A pocket full of posies.
A-tishoo! A-tishoo!
We all fall down.

This rhyme refers to a terrible **epidemic** that was known as 'The Great Plague'. In 1665, a disease called **bubonic plague** spread through the whole of Britain. It killed many thousands of people. Though originally spread by rats, it was transmitted rapidly between people.

The first **symptoms** of bubonic plague were circles of red spots on the skin. These developed into swellings called **boils** or 'buboes', which eventually burst. As the disease progressed, the sufferer would sneeze and cough violently. Finally, the sufferer would die.

Many people believed that carrying flowers to 'purify' the air around them would protect them from the Plague. It did not. A more effective strategy was to isolate those infected so that they could not pass on the disease. The people of Eyam, in Derbyshire, cut their village off completely to avoid infecting the villages around – a brave act that saved many lives in that region.

Can you explain what each line in the rhyme means?

Line 1: _____

_____

Line 2: _____

_____

Line 3: _____

_____

Line 4: _____

_____

Find out more about the Great Plague and how people tried to control the spread of the disease. Write a diary of someone who visited an area where the Plague was prevalent.

Prevent or cure?

There is an old saying: Prevention is better than cure.
Explain what this means. Think about diseases. _____

_____

_____

Look at these pictures.

1.    2.    3.

Explain how each picture shows good behaviour for preventing the spread
of disease. Think about what might happen if these actions were not taken.

1. _____

_____

2. _____

_____

3. _____

_____

Some newborn babies need to be placed in an incubator for a few days.
How does this help to stop them becoming ill?

_____

_____

When babies are very young, they are fed milk from a bottle. This milk, the
bottle and the teat used for feeding all need to be **sterilised**.

What does 'sterilised' mean? _____

_____

Why is it important for preventing disease? _____

_____

_____

Useful microbes

The **bacteria** that cause decay make our food go rotten. However, they are useful because they clear up waste material. **Soil bacteria** break down (decay) the dead bodies of plants and animals, and release **chemicals** from these bodies for other **organisms** to use. Dead plants and animals would pile up forever if microbes did not act on them. Bacteria also grow and feed on various materials that we throw away, such as paper and fabrics.

We use bacteria to make food for us – for example, turning milk into **cheese** and **yoghurt**. We use a **fungus** called **yeast** to make bread, wine and beer. The main **ingredients** needed to make bread are flour and water (to form dough) and sugar. Yeast feeds on the sugar to turn it into a gas which forms little bubbles inside the dough. The gas cannot escape, so the dough swells or rises. This works best in a warm place.

These days, we use microbes to make a variety of foods, chemicals, medicines, fuels and even plastics. Perhaps, one day, microbes will help us to create more food in order to feed the world's people and make everyone more healthy. But we can't leave it all to microbes. We have to be responsible in how we use, **recycle** and **conserve** the resources that we have.

Useful microbes

1. Name two materials that are decayed by microbes.

_____ and _____

2. When is decay useful?_____

_____

3. Name two foods that are produced with the help of bacteria.

a) _____ b) _____

4. Which type of microbe is used to make bread and beer? _____

Name another drink made by these microbes. _____

Are yeast organisms bacteria? Write 'Yes' or 'No'. _____

5. Sugar is an important ingredient for making bread. Explain what

happens to it. _____

_____

6. Microbes are used nowadays to make various things. Name three of

these things. _____ _____ _____

7. Leaves fall off trees in the autumn. Chemicals from the dead leaves may
be taken back into the tree through its roots and used for making new
leaves. Explain how microbes help in this process.

_____

_____

_____

What does **'biodegradable'** mean? Write an article for a science magazine
about how important microbes are in our environment. Use these ideas to
persuade your readers to use biodegradable materials.

Useful microbes

1. Underline the materials that are decayed by microbes.

> glass   paper   steel   wool   tin

2. When is decay useful? _____

_____

3. Name two foods that are produced with the help of bacteria.

a) _____   b) _____

4. Which microbes are used to make bread and beer? _____

Name another drink made by these microbes. _____

Are yeast organisms bacteria? Answer 'Yes' or 'No'. _____

5. When bread is made, yeast attacks sugar to produce a gas. What

happens next? _____

6. Microbes are used nowadays to make various things. Name three of

these things. _____   _____   _____

7. What happens when a leaf falls from a tree in autumn? Write 'True' or
'False' after each sentence.

The leaf on the ground is decayed by microbes.   _____

Chemicals are set free from the roots.   _____

The chemicals are absorbed by the roots.   _____

The chemicals rise through the tree to make new leaves.   _____

What does **'biodegradable'** mean? Write an article for a science newsletter
about how important microbes are in our environment. Use these ideas to
persuade your readers to use biodegradable materials.

Microbes to the rescue

Bacteria are very small living organisms. They can reproduce very quickly in the right conditions. They can be killed by heat. Some bacteria can cause diseases, but others can be very useful if controlled and used properly.

The five sentences in each paragraph of the passage below have been mixed up. Can you sort them out? Rewrite the paragraphs, with the sentences in the correct order, on another sheet of paper.

The history of penicillin

He was about to throw the dishes away when he noticed that all the bacteria around the spots of mould had died. In 1928, a Scottish scientist called Alexander Fleming noticed mould growing on some dishes where he was trying to grow cultures of bacteria. Something in the mould was killing the bacteria. Penicillin was discovered by accident. The dishes had become contaminated with mould spores from the air.

Antibiotics have been very important in helping people to fight all kinds of bacterial infections. Fleming called this type of mould 'penicillin'. Ten years later, two scientists called Howard Florey and Ernest Chain developed a form of penicillin that could be swallowed. He made a liquid from it that could be applied to wounds in order to stop bacteria infecting them. Penicillin was the first **antibiotic** – a medicine that uses microbes to kill bacteria.

Use books and CD-ROMs to find information about the history of sewage disposal. Answer these questions:
1. What are the disadvantages of burying sewage in the ground?
2. What are the disadvantages of pouring sewage into the sea?
3. How are bacteria used nowadays to make sewage less dangerous?

How large is a microbe?

This line is one
decimetre long. _____
There are ten of these in 1 metre, which is a little more than the
distance around the four edges of this page. Check and see!

This line is one **centimetre** long.   ____
There are ten of these in the first line above. Check to make sure.

This line is one **millimetre** long.   -
There are ten of these in the second line above. So there are 1000
millimetres in 1 metre.

A **micrometre** is too small to see. There are 1000 micrometres in 1
millimetre. So there are a million micrometres in 1 metre. The prefix
'micro' means 'one-millionth part of'.

Micro-organisms, also known as microbes, are very small. They are
much too small for the naked eye to see them. We need very powerful
microscopes to see microbes. Yet these tiny living things are extremely
important to our lives.

1. Find out how big (how tall or long) each of these organisms is: an
elephant, a hamster, an ant and a microbe (for example, a bacillus). Work
out how much bigger each organism is than the next biggest one.

_____

_____

_____

_____

2. Which organism do you think is the most dangerous to people in a jungle:
tigers, snakes or malaria microbes? Explain your answer.

_____

_____

Making bread

Microbes work busily, quietly and out of sight. One way in which they work for us is in the process of making bread. Bread is an important item in a healthy diet.

Write 'bread' under the name of its main contribution to our diet.

| protein | carbohydrate | fat | fibre | minerals | vitamins |

_____

On another sheet of paper, write a set of instructions for making a loaf of bread. The ingredients you need are listed below. Remember to say how much time is needed (where appropriate). Explain where the action of the microbes happens.

350g plain flour

5g margarine

1 teaspoon salt

25g fresh yeast

210ml tepid milk and water

Foods that make the same contribution to our diet as bread are known as 'staple foods'. Name three other staple foods.

1. _____

2. _____

3. _____

Find out about some different kinds of bread, such as naan bread, chapattis and matzo bread.
● What are their ingredients?
● How are they made?
● Write a recipe sheet for three different kinds of bread.

▲SCHOLASTIC

How plants reproduce

Flowering plants use their **flowers** to make **seeds** which can grow into new plants. Seeds are made by **sexual reproduction**. The sex **organs** of a plant are parts of its flowers.

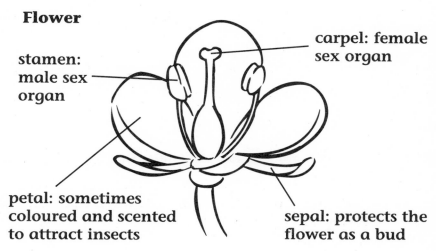

Flower

stamen: male sex organ

carpel: female sex organ

petal: sometimes coloured and scented to attract insects

sepal: protects the flower as a bud

The first stage in making new seeds is **pollination**. This happens when the male sex cells or **pollen grains** are carried from the **anther** of one plant to the **stigma** of another plant.

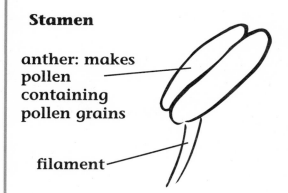

Stamen

anther: makes pollen containing pollen grains

filament

The pollen grains of flowers such as buttercups and dandelions are carried by insects (such as bees). These flowers have large **petals** that are coloured and **scented** to **attract** the insects, and the pollen **grains** are large and spiked to stick to the insect's body.

The pollen grains of plants such as grasses and catkins are spread by the wind. These pollen grains are small and light, so the wind can carry them. Wind-pollinated plants produce more pollen than insect-pollinated plants.

After pollination, the next stage in making new seeds is **fertilisation**. This happens in the **ovary**, where a male sex cell joins up with the female sex cell or **ovule** to form a seed. A pollen grain attached to the **stigma** grows a tube into the ovary to fertilise the ovule. The ovary then develops into a **fruit** around the seed.

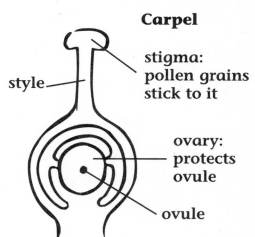

Carpel

stigma: pollen grains stick to it

style

ovary: protects ovule

ovule

How plants reproduce

1. Which part of a plant produces its seeds? _____

2. What is the name of:
● the male sex organ of a flower? _____
● the male sex cell of a flower? _____
● the female sex organ of a flower? _____

3. What is the job of the sepals? _____
_____

4. Write 'True' or 'False' after each of these sentences.

Flowers pollinated by insects have coloured petals. _____
Grasses are pollinated by insects. _____
Flowers pollinated by insects have small pollen grains. _____
Buttercups have large scented petals. _____
Catkins produce large numbers of pollen grains. _____

5. If a flower were damaged and lost its anther, what might be the
consequence? _____
_____

6. Give two examples of flowers that are:
● pollinated by insects 1. _____ 2. _____
● pollinated by wind   1. _____ 2. _____

7. Describe what happens after a pollen grain lands on a stigma.
_____
_____

Describe how pollination happens in a buttercup plant and a catkin plant.
What features do these two plants have that make each plant's method of
pollination easy?

How plants reproduce

1. Which part of a plant produces its seeds? _____

2. Draw lines to match these words to their definitions.

   pollen grain   the male sex organ of a flower

   carpel   the male sex cell of a flower

   stamen   the female sex organ of a flower

3. When do the sepals protect the petals?

   _____

4. Write 'True' or 'False' after each sentence.

   Flowers pollinated by insects have coloured petals. _____
   Grasses are pollinated by insects. _____
   Flowers pollinated by insects have small pollen grains. _____
   Buttercups have large scented petals. _____
   Catkins produce large numbers of pollen grains. _____

5. Pollination happens when pollen is carried from an anther to a stigma. If a flower were damaged and lost its anther, what consequence might this have?

   _____

6. Give two examples of flowering plants that are:
   - pollinated by insects   1. _____   2. _____
   - pollinated by wind   1. _____   2. _____

7. Use the words in this list to complete the sentences below.

stigma	female	fruit	inside	seed	pollination

   After a pollen grain lands on a _____, the next step is _____.

   A male sex cell joins up with a _____ sex cell to form a _____.

   Fertilisation occurs _____ the ovary, which becomes a _____.

   How are a buttercup plant and a catkin plant pollinated? Explain how each plant is suited to its method of pollination.

Coded messages

The answers to these questions about plant reproduction are written in code. Can you crack the code?

What is made?   ofx qmbou   _____

How does it happen?   gdsujmjtbujpo   _____

What happens first?   qpmmjobujpo   _____

Where from?   bouifs   _____

Where to?   tujhnb   _____

What is the carrier?   jotfdu   _____

Use the same code to name a different type of carrier.

Other type of carrier: _____

Use the code to name a suitable plant for each type of carrier.

The first carrier works best for a _____

The second carrier works best for a _____

Explain in ordinary language why the second carrier is best for the plant you have named. _____

_____

_____

_____

◖SCHOLASTIC   DEVELOPING SCIENCE LANGUAGE for Living Things 10-11

Bees and pollination

Read this poem and think about what it means.

Forget not bees in winter,
though they sleep.
For winter's big
with summer in her womb.

Vita Sackville-West

Why do you think this poem is called 'Spring'? _____

_____

_____

How does the poem describe what bees do in pollination?

_____

_____

_____

_____

Write your own short poem about wind pollination. Make notes in the box below, then write your poem on another sheet of paper.

Flowery language

By the end of this year, she'll have blossomed.

He's been a busy bee lately.

She's rather a delicate bloom.

He's a budding musician.

Her family has deep roots in this town.

These statements are not literally true. They are examples of metaphors. A metaphor is when you describe something by calling it something else.

Use what you know about plants to explain what each of the statements means. The first one has been done for you.

1. 'He's a budding musician' means that his skill is still developing, like a bud that will become a flower.

2. 'Her family has deep roots in this town' means _____

_____

_____

3. 'By the end of this year, she'll have blossomed' means _____

_____

_____

4. 'He's been a busy bee lately' means _____

_____

_____

5. 'She's rather a delicate bloom' means _____

_____

_____

Seeds, fruits, dispersal

Most plants produce hundreds of seeds at a time. If they all fell to the ground close to the parent plant, the new plants would grow too close together. There would be **overcrowding**. The new plants would have to **compete** with each other for water, **minerals** and light. As a result, many of the young plants would not grow.

To avoid overcrowding, seeds are **scattered** from the parent plant in various ways. This process is called **seed dispersal**. It is carried out by the wind, by animals or by the parent plant itself.

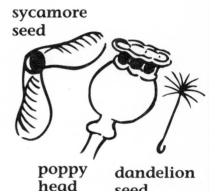

sycamore seed

poppy head   dandelion seed

Dandelion and thistle seeds have a downy parachute that is blown about by the wind. Sycamore, ash and lime seeds have 'wings' that enable them to travel long distances in the wind. Poppy heads sway in the wind and scatter seeds through holes in their sides.

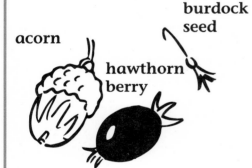

burdock seed

acorn

hawthorn berry

Blackberry and hawthorn berries are eaten by animals. The seeds pass through the animal and are dropped at some distance from the parent plant. The burdock seed has hooks that catch on animal fur. Acorns and nuts are carried away by squirrels and birds.

Coconuts are carried far away by currents in the sea.

coconut

Some plants do their own dispersal. Lupin and geranium seed-pods burst open when they are dry and scatter their seeds.

lupin pod

Some seeds are collected by gardeners or farmers and then scattered. For example, a farmer will harvest grain in the autumn and keep some to sow for the next year, while the rest is ground up into flour.

Seeds, fruits, dispersal

1.   What does 'seed dispersal' mean? _____
_____

2.   Give three reasons why seeds need to be dispersed.

a) _____

b) _____

c) _____

3.   Name two plants that use the wind to disperse their seeds.

a) _____   b) _____

4.   Choose one of the two plants from question 3 and describe how its
seeds are well **adapted** for dispersal by the wind.

_____

_____

5.   Do these plants use animals to disperse their seeds? Write 'Yes' or 'No'.

a) Burdock _____   b) Poppy _____   c) Blackberry _____

d) Acorn _____   e) Lupin _____

6.   How are poppy seeds dispersed? _____

_____

7.   Name two plants that explode to disperse their seeds.

a) _____   b) _____

8.   What type of material in your clothes would make you a good disperser

of seeds? Explain your answer. _____

_____

Choose one of the plants mentioned in the text. Find out more about it,
then write a factfile with these three headings: 1. Where does it grow best?
2. When does it grow best? 3. When and how does it disperse its seeds?

Seeds, fruits, dispersal

1. What does 'seed dispersal' mean? _____

_____

2. Write 'True' or 'False' after each sentence.
Seeds need to be dispersed to prevent overcrowding. _____
Overcrowding would stop some plants having enough light. _____

3. Name two plants that use the wind to disperse their seeds.
a) _____ b) _____

4. What is special about the seeds of the sycamore plant? Explain how
this helps them to be scattered by the wind. _____

_____

_____

5. Do these plants use animals to disperse their seeds? Write 'Yes' or 'No'.
a) Burdock _____   b) Poppy _____   c) Blackberry _____
d) Acorn _____   e) Lupin _____

6. How are poppy seeds dispersed? _____

_____

_____

7. The lupin seed-pod explodes to disperse its
seeds. Name another plant seed-pod that explodes. _____

8. If you rubbed against a burdock plant, would wearing a smooth plastic
jacket help you to disperse its seeds? Explain your answer.

_____

_____

Choose one of the plants mentioned in the text. Find out more about it,
then write a factfile with these three headings: 1. Where does it grow best?
2. When does it grow best? 3. When and how does it disperse its seeds?

Seedy chat

These statements are examples of metaphors (see page 64). In each case, something is being described by using an image to do with plants or seeds.

Use what you know about plants to explain what each statement means.

1. 'You've planted the seeds of trouble' means _____

_____

_____

2. 'Their plans haven't borne fruit' means _____

_____

_____

3. 'We can see the green shoots of recovery' means _____

_____

_____

4. 'My suggestions fell on stony ground' means _____

_____

_____

SCHOLASTIC   DEVELOPING SCIENCE LANGUAGE for Living Things 10–11

How are the seeds dispersed?

These pictures show some types of fruits with seeds.

Describe how the seeds from each fruit are dispersed. Explain how each seed is suited to its method of dispersal.

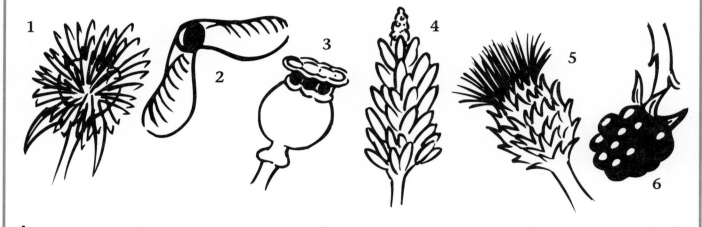

1. _____

_____

_____

2. _____

_____

_____

3. _____

_____

_____

4. _____

_____

_____

5. _____

_____

_____

6. _____

_____

_____

A key for seeds and fruits

These pictures show the seeds or fruits of six different types of plants.

We can use a **key** to identify seeds or fruits as belonging to a particular type or **species** of plant. The key asks questions to help us distinguish between the features of different seeds or fruits. For example, a key might start with:

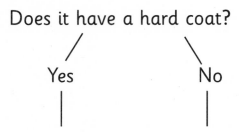

Does it have a hard coat?

Yes   No

On another sheet of paper, write a key to help your friend work out which plant each seed or fruit belongs to.

Swap sheets with your friend. Can he or she use your key to identify the type of plant that each seed or fruit belongs to?

Roots, minerals, soils

Many plants need **soil** to **anchor** their roots and to provide them with water and **minerals**. Soil is therefore necessary for most animals on land, since they eat the plants that grow in soil or other animals that eat those plants.

Soil is a mixture of small pieces of rock and **humus**, which is the decayed remains of dead plants and animals. The rock is broken down into tiny pieces by **weathering**.

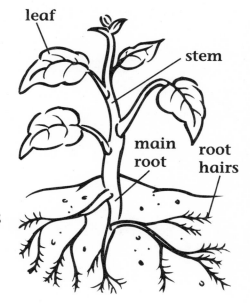

leaf

stem

main root

root hairs

In a **fertile** soil (a soil that is good for plants to grow in), tiny rock particles are stuck together by humus to form small crumbs. These crumbs slowly release mineral salts, which are **chemicals** containing minerals. These soak up water. There are spaces between the crumbs where the **roots** of plants can grow to obtain water, **dissolved** minerals and air.

Towards its tip, each root has many fine **root hairs**. These spread out in the soil spaces to absorb water and mineral **nutrients**. Dissolved minerals move upwards through the roots to the stem, and through the stem to the leaves and flowers.

Plants need a regular supply of small amounts of minerals for healthy growth. When their plants have used up most of the **stock** of minerals in the soil and need more, gardeners often add **fertiliser** to the soil. Fertilisers are usually made from the decayed remains of plants and animals. They **replenish** the stock of minerals so that the plants can take in the right amounts.

Roots, minerals, soils

1. Give two reasons why land plants need soil.

a) _____

b) _____

2. Why do land animals depend on soil? _____

_____

_____

3. What two materials make up soil?

a) _____   b) _____

4. What three substances do roots obtain from soil?

a) _____   b) _____   c) _____

5. If there were no spaces between the crumbs of soil, would it be easy for plants to grow there? Explain your answer.

_____

_____

6. On another sheet, draw and label a diagram to show the journey of water through a plant. Use a blue pen to show the route of the water.

7. Plants make their own food. So why do gardeners often need to give their plants some 'plant food'?

_____

_____

_____

In the 17th century, a scientist called van Helmont did an experiment. He weighed some soil and put it in a pot. Then he weighed a small willow plant and put it in the soil in the pot. For five years he watered the plant, but did nothing else to it. After five years, he repeated the weighings. He found that the soil weighed the same as before, but the willow was heavier.

Try to explain this result.

Roots, minerals, soils

1. Write 'True' or 'False' after each sentence.

a) Land plants need soil for support. _____

b) Land plants get minerals from soil. _____

c) Land plants get water from the air. _____

2. Why do land animals depend on soil? _____

_____

_____

3. Cross out the incorrect words in brackets in these sentences.

Soil is made from (small / big) pieces of (rock / wood).

(Rock / Humus) is the (decayed / living) remains of plants and animals.

4. What three substances do roots obtain from soil?

a) _____ b) _____ c) _____

5. Complete this sentence.

The spaces between rock crumbs enable roots to _____

6. On another sheet of paper, draw a diagram to show the journey of water through a plant. Use a blue pen to show the route of the water. Label the place where the water starts and the plant parts that it moves through.

7. What are fertilisers made from? _____

What are they used for? _____

_____

In the 17th century, a scientist called van Helmont did an experiment. He weighed some soil and put it in a pot. Then he weighed a small willow plant and put it in the soil in the pot. For five years he watered the plant, but did nothing else to it. After five years, he repeated the weighings. He found that the soil weighed the same as before, but the willow was heavier.

Try to explain this result. Think about what the plant needs to grow.

Which growing material is best?

Adam and Sakina wanted to find out which of several growing materials would be the best for their plants.

Their teacher gave them these items:
- a tin with tiny holes in the bottom
- a stopwatch
- an empty milk bottle.

They were also given bags of sand, gravel, clay and a mystery material (which was actually garden soil). They were able to work at a sink with a water tap.

On another sheet of paper, write a plan for their investigation. Write your plan in the form of numbered instructions. Remember to say how Sakina and Adam can use their results to decide which material would be the best for growing plants in.

Use the pictures below to help you write the first three instructions.

1. 2. 3.

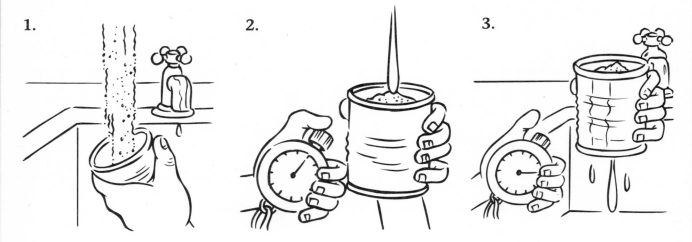

Which material do you think will be the best for growing plants in? Explain your answer.

_____

_____

_____

Field survey

Some children were doing a survey of the different types of plants in a field.
They decided to count how many plants of six main types were growing
inside five hoops that they put down at random in the field. This is what they
recorded.

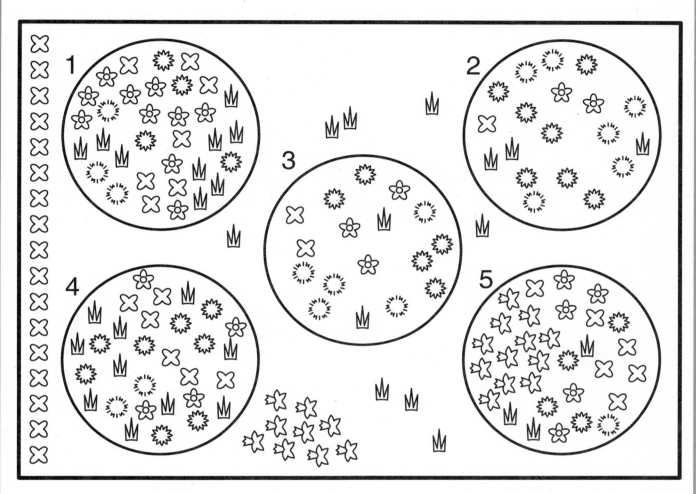

This key shows the symbols the children used for different plants.

Write a report about the children's survey on another sheet of paper.
● Show their results in a table.
● Make some comments about how the different types of plants are
distributed (spread around) in the field.
● Do you think all the plants are wild? Could some of the plants have been
grown there deliberately by people?

The mystery of the onion plants

Two next-door neighbours, Katy and James, decided to grow some onions in their gardens. They did not want many, so they shared a single packet of onion seeds.

After a few weeks, the onions in the two gardens looked like this.

Explain why the onion plants in the two gardens were so different.

_____

_____

_____

_____

Choose one of your suggestions and plan an investigation that you might carry out to test whether the suggestion is correct. Write your plan on another sheet of paper. These questions may help you:

● What will you need?
● What will you change?
● What will you keep the same?
● What will you measure?

Pure water

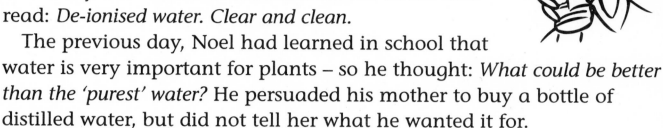

Noel was in his family's car when they stopped at a garage. While his mother was putting petrol in the car, Noel browsed in the shop. His attention was caught by a sign that said: *Only the purest, distilled water for your car battery.* He looked at the label on the bottle and read: *De-ionised water. Clear and clean.*

The previous day, Noel had learned in school that water is very important for plants – so he thought: *What could be better than the 'purest' water?* He persuaded his mother to buy a bottle of distilled water, but did not tell her what he wanted it for.

The next day, Noel asked his teacher if he could do an investigation with the plants that he had ready for growing. He took two pots with the same amount of soil in each. In each pot, the shoots of cress seeds were just beginning to grow above the surface of the soil. His investigation was to compare the effects of water from the tap and his new 'pure' water.

After some days, much to his surprise, Noel found that the plants receiving 'pure' water were not growing as well as the ones receiving tap water.
'Try adding some of this,' Noel's teacher said, 'but read the label first.' He gave Noel a small bottle. This is what Noel read on the label: *Nitrogen 15%, Phosphorus Pentoxide 30%, Potassium Oxide 15%, Boron 0.02%, Iron 0.15%, Copper 0.07%, Manganese 0.05%, Zinc 0.06%.*

Noel tried growing more plants and adding some of the liquid from the bottle. He found that the plants grew well this time.

Answer these questions on another sheet of paper.
1. Why did the plants receiving 'pure' water grow less well than the ones receiving tap water?
2. Why did the liquid from the small bottle help the plants to grow? Think about what a plant needs from soil.

How a root grows

Some pupils investigated what happens when a seed germinates. This is what they wrote.

We left some dried peas in water for about two days. Then we wrapped them in moist blotting paper.

After three days, we unrolled the blotting paper and saw that each pea had a root about 10mm long.

We had heard that the root did not grow by the same amounts at all places along its length. We investigated this by marking the root and leaving it in a dish for two days.

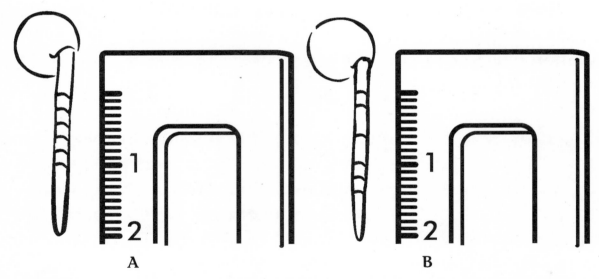

Diagram A shows how the root looked at the start. Diagram B shows how it looked after two days.

That is all they wrote. Can you finish their report for them on another sheet of paper? You will need to do the following:

1. Describe the first pattern of marks.
2. Describe the second pattern of marks.
3. Draw a graph to show the two patterns of marks.
4. Explain what the graph shows about how different parts of the root grow. It might help if you look at the distances between the first three marks in each pattern.

What plants need

When seeds fall from their parent plant, they are **dispersed** (**scattered**) over a wide area. This helps to prevent **overcrowding** and **competition** for the best conditions (light, water, soil) in which to grow.

Many seeds are able to **survive** in conditions that are not suitable for growth, such as **severe** winters and **drought**. They do this by going into a **dormant** state, which means that they appear to be dead but will grow later when conditions improve.

Seeds **germinate** (begin to grow) in warm, damp soil. The seed **absorbs** (takes in) water, which makes it swell. The water also softens the hard coat around the seed. As a result, the coat splits open. Water, air and **minerals** from the soil help to change the food stored in the seed, so that **energy** can be released for growth.

The young plant forms tiny roots that grow out through the seed's coat and into the soil. The roots **anchor** the plant and take in water and minerals from the soil. A young **shoot** develops and grows upwards through the soil and into the air and light. After a while, green leaves appear on the shoot. The leaves use sunlight to make food by **photosynthesis** for the growing plant.

What happens to a seed

plant

fertilisation
– pollen from another flower

seeds

germination
– water
– soil
– warmth
– light

dispersal
– self
– wind
– animals

dormancy
– winter
– drought

What plants need

1. Give two reasons why seeds need to be scattered.

    a) _____

    b) _____

2. What is a **dormant** seed? _____

    _____

3. What science word means 'start to grow'?

    _____

4. What four things help a seed to grow?

    a) _____   b) _____

    c) _____   d) _____

5. Why do seeds need to store food? _____

    _____

    _____

6. Germination does not usually take place in the depth of winter. Explain
    why not. _____

    _____

7. Give two reasons why young plants need roots.

    a) _____

    b) _____

8. What function (job) do the green leaves have? _____

    _____

A newspaper reported recently that some corn seeds grew successfully
after they had been stored in an Egyptian tomb for thousands of years.
Explain how this can happen.

What plants need

1. Give two reasons why seeds need to be scattered.

a) _____

b) _____

2. Dormant seeds appear to be dead. True or false? _____

3. What science word is used about seeds and means 'starts to grow'?

_____

4. What four things help a seed to grow in the soil?

a) _____   b) _____

c) _____   d) _____

5. Cross out the incorrect words in the brackets in this sentence.
Seeds need a (water / food) store that can be used to release
(energy / water) for growth.

6. Underline the correct words in the brackets in this sentence.
Germination does not take place in the (winter / summer) because
it is (dark / cold).

7. Why do young plants need roots? Give two reasons.

a) _____

b) _____

8. What job (**'function'** is the science word) is done by the green leaves?

_____

_____

A newspaper reported recently that some corn seeds grew successfully
after they had been stored in an Egyptian tomb for thousands of years.
Explain how this can happen.

The sower of seeds

There is a traditional story about a man in a hot country who was sowing seeds to grow grain for food. In those days, seeds were simply thrown as the sower walked along.

The story tells what happened to the seeds that fell onto four types of ground. Some seeds fell on the pathway. Some seeds fell on rocky ground with some soil in the cracks between stones. Some seeds fell among thorny bushes. Some seeds fell onto fertile soil.

Describe what you think happened to the seeds in each group. Use your science knowledge to explain why.

The seeds that fell on the pathway _____

_____

_____

The seeds that fell on rocky ground _____

_____

_____

The seeds that fell among thorny bushes _____

_____

_____

The seeds that fell onto fertile soil _____

_____

_____

If you read the story, you can find out what the storyteller said happened to the seeds. The story is in the Bible (the Book of Luke, Chapter 8, verses 5–8).

Looking after cut flowers

Look at this picture of a vase of flowers.

Put a tick (✓) by the statement that gives the best description of what the picture shows.

Put a star (★) by the statement that gives the most reasonable explanation of what you see in the picture.

There is no water in the vase.

The family have gone away.

There are drooping flowers in the vase.

It is too hot in the room.

The flowers are too heavy for the stems.

Why do you think cut flowers need to be kept in water? Think about how water travels through a plant.

_____

_____

_____

Why is it necessary to change the water every day? Think about what plants need to be healthy.

_____

_____

_____

Look at a packet of 'flower food' from a florist's shop. Answer these questions on another sheet of paper:

1.   What do you think the packet contains?
2.   Why do you think the packet tell you to:
a)   dissolve the contents in water before use?
b)   avoid brushing or breaking the stems of the flowers that you place in the flower food solution?

Do leaves lose water?

Omar and Iestyn are studying the behaviour of leaves. They want to know whether leaves take up water from the stem and lose it to the air.

This is their plan for the investigation.

What we will use

Three bottles with narrow necks, a twig with leaves, a similar twig without leaves, a water tap.

What we will do

1. Use three milk bottles of the same volume.

2. Put the same volume of water in each bottle.

3. Use twigs from different trees.

4. Use twigs of the same length and diameter.

5. Remove all the leaves from one twig, but leave all the leaves on the other twig.

6. Put each twig in a bottle.

7. Close up the necks to prevent loss by evaporation.

8. Leave one bottle sealed without any twig.

9. Mark where the water levels are at the start of the study.

10. Mark where the water levels are at various times during the following week.

What we predict will happen

1. The water levels in the three bottles will be different.

2. More water will be lost through the bare twig than through the leafy twig, because none of the water is needed to keep leaves green.

Answer these questions on another sheet.

1. Describe what Iestyn and Omar have done to make their test fair.
2. Is there something else that they should have done to make their test fair?
3. Do you agree with both of their predictions? Explain your answer.
4. Plan an experiment to find out how quickly water is lost from the leaves. Here's a clue: small plastic bags may be useful.

Saving water

All plants need a steady supply of water and minerals.

Does 'minerals' mean lumps of rock? If not, what does it mean?

_____

If the water supply to an environment becomes very small or becomes **polluted**, the plants and animals there will not be healthy. Many of them will die, and some types of plants or animals might even become **extinct**. Animals can usually move from place to place in search of water, but plants cannot. That is why we have to care for our plants.

Although a lot of rain falls in Britain each year, a great deal is wasted or misused. We all need to look after the supply of water – a very special liquid that all living things depend on for their life and health.

These pictures show three ways of not wasting water in our gardens.

Use these pictures to write three instructions for gardeners.

1. _____

_____

2. _____

_____

3. _____

_____

Write a letter to the Environment Agency for your area, asking for information about wildlife sites that are at risk because of lack of water.

Plants need light

Shahid had learned that plants need light, water and minerals from the soil to grow well. He decided to investigate the need of plants for light.

Shahid wrote down these questions for himself:

●   How powerful should the light be?

●   Would an ordinary electric lamp help?

●   Plants don't die in the night, so how long do they need light for?

●   Which colour of light is best? Is orange best? (He remembered seeing road workers wearing orange jackets in order to be seen clearly.)

Try to help Shahid by writing a plan for his investigation. Use these headings to help you get started.

I'll study this question:

I'll use this equipment:

I'll follow this method:

This is what I think will happen:

Local studies

There are many different **habitats**. These are places where **communities** of plants and animals live and **interact** with each other. The animals (**consumers**) depend on the plants (**producers**) for food.

Food chains and **food webs** are diagrams that show how the **energy** from food passes from one **organism** to another in a habitat.

A convenient outdoor habitat to study is the **leaf litter** under a tree in autumn. Dead leaves, twigs and fruits cover the ground, providing food and shelter for many animals.

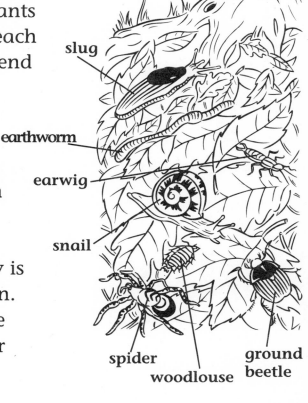

A freshwater **aquarium** is another habitat that is easy to study and quite simple to **maintain** indoors. It can be set up in a tank, and various organisms can be collected from different places to put in it. Remember to ask adults for advice before you collect organisms from their natural **environment**. You should return the animals to their environment when you have finished your **observations**.

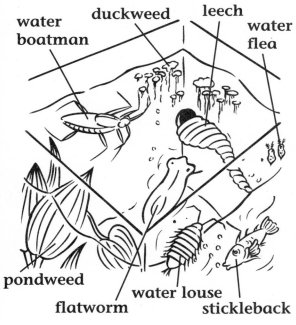

The aquarium must have plenty of plants to produce food and **oxygen** for the other organisms in the community. There should not be too many animals in the aquarium. This is because they (the consumers) might eat all the plants (the producers) and so destroy the food chains.

Local studies

1. What is the difference between a **community** and a **habitat**?

   _____

   _____

2. Why are green plants known as **producers**? _____

   _____

   Why are animals known as **consumers**? _____

   _____

3. What do the arrows in a food chain show? _____

   _____

   Write a food chain for these members of a community.

   a) duck, pondweed, pond snail

   $\Rightarrow$ $\Rightarrow$

   b) earthworm, dead leaves, bird

   $\Rightarrow$ $\Rightarrow$

4. Why is it important to keep plenty of plants in an aquarium, but not too many animals? _____

   _____

   _____

5. From the organisms in the aquarium, write two food chains that end with a stickleback.

   $\Rightarrow$ $\Rightarrow$ stickleback

   $\Rightarrow$ $\Rightarrow$ stickleback

   It is necessary to change the water in an aquarium from time to time. Your friend has asked you: 'Should I add tap water, rain water, pond water or sea water?' Write a letter to tell your friend what to do and explain why.

Local studies

1. Cross out the incorrect word in the brackets in each sentence.
A (habitat / community) is a place where plants and animals live.
Plants and animals live and interact with each other to form a
(community / habitat).

2. Why are green plants known as **producers**? _____

_____

Why are animals known as **consumers**? _____

_____

3. The arrows in a food chain show how energy
moves from one organism to another. True or false? _____

Write a food chain for these members of a community.

a)   duck, pondweed, pond snail

⇨   ⇨

b)   earthworm, dead leaves, bird

⇨   ⇨

4. What would happen if you had too many animals and not enough

plants in an aquarium? _____

_____

_____

5. From the picture of an aquarium, write two food chains that start with
duckweed and end with a stickleback.

duckweed   ⇨   ⇨   stickleback

duckweed   ⇨   ⇨   stickleback

It is necessary to change the water in an aquarium from time to time. Your
friend has asked you: 'Should I add tap water, rain water, pond water or sea
water?' Write a letter to tell your friend what kind of water to use. Explain
why you think it is the best kind of water for the aquarium.

The white owl

After doing a study of her local area, Mary wrote a factfile about owls. She included this verse from the poem 'The Owl' by Alfred, Lord Tennyson.

> When cats run home and light is come,
> And dew is cold upon the ground,
> And the far-off stream is dumb,
> And the whirring sail goes round,
> And the whirring sail goes round;
> Alone and warming his five wits,
> The white owl in the belfry sits.

What situation is described in the first line? _____

What kind of substance is dew? _____
_____

How is it formed? _____
_____

What is the 'whirring sail'? _____

What are the owl's 'five wits'? List them. _____
_____

Why do you think the owl sleeps by day and hunts by night?
_____

What is the science word for animals that are only active at night?
_____

Write another verse for this poem, describing the same scene at night.

SCHOLASTIC

Classifying animals

After going for a walk across some fields and into a forest, Jake and Laura came back to school very tired.

Their teacher said, 'That was interesting, wasn't it?'

'Yes,' said Jake, 'but very confusing.'

'Oh,' said the teacher. 'Why was it confusing?'

'Well,' Jake started to speak, but Laura interrupted.

'It's my turn now.' She looked at the teacher and said, 'We saw lots of animals. Some have fur, some have feathers. Some are slimy, some are dry. I know they are all animals, but they just don't seem to be the same.'

'Not to worry,' said their teacher. 'Scientists have a plan to **classify** animals into groups, so they can tell which animals are which.' She drew this plan:

All animals

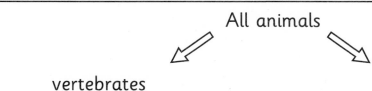

vertebrates   invertebrates, such as:

mammals birds fish reptiles amphibians   worms arthropods molluscs

'That's better,' said Jake. 'Now we can sort out what we saw. I know what *vertebrate* means.'

'Well?' asked Laura when Jake did not said anything more.

'It means… I've forgotten,' groaned Jake.

'Never mind,' said Laura. 'We can use the scientists' plan.'

'There's just one snag. We don't know what the different names mean.'

'Don't be silly,' said Laura. 'You know what birds and fish are.'

'But we must be like scientists and try to be precise,' protested Jake.

2 Classifying animals

Read the sheet 'Classifying animals (1)'.
Can you help Jake by explaining what a vertebrate is?

_____

_____

Laura and Jake spoke to their teacher about their problem with classifying the animals they had seen. She gave them some cards. 'One set of cards shows the names of groups of vertebrates,' she explained, 'and the other set shows the features that each group have. Can you match the sets?'

These are some of the cards. Fill in the blank cards. Draw a line to match the name of each group to the correct list of features.

mammals	
fish	They have scales and gills.
reptiles	They have feathers and lay eggs with hard shells.

On another sheet of paper, write a description of one animal in each of the five groups of vertebrates. Explain how its features show which group it belongs to.

Teacher instructions
The completed cards can be used for a matching game with pairs of children, a group or the whole class. The activity could be extended by creating similar cards for the three invertebrate groups listed on page 91.

Vertebrate groups

Here are some pictures of different vertebrates. Under each picture, write one of the words in this list to show which group the animal belongs to.

fish   amphibian   reptile   bird   mammal

elephant	lion	tortoise	human
snake	crocodile	frog	eagle
seagull	giraffe	whale	shark
goldfish	newt	penguin	lizard
turtle	toad	cow	salamander
trout	robin	swan	cat

Think about a river (and river bank) as a habitat. Which of the vertebrates shown above might live there?

_____

_____

How many of the five vertebrate groups appear in your list? _____
Discuss with your teacher what your answer tells you about vertebrate life.

Crusoe's island

Have you read *Robinson Crusoe* by Daniel Defoe? If so, you will remember that Crusoe lived on an island. If you do not know this book, try to find it. It's a good tale.

We can guess that Crusoe probably spent a good deal of time walking up and down the beach. He probably saw a lot of different living things on the seashore. He may have seen these:

seagull   starfish   lobster   jellyfish

sand eel   razorshell   periwinkle   crab

kelp   barnacle   limpet   sea anemone

Imagine that Crusoe wanted to know the names of these living things. There was nobody on the island to ask and he had no reference books. So he decided to write descriptions of them in a letter, put the letter in a bottle and throw it into the sea.

What might he have written? Write descriptions of three living things that are shown above. Do not write their names.

1. _____

_____

2. _____

_____

3. _____

_____

Swap sheets with a friend. Can you name the animals your friend has described?

1. _____ 2. _____ 3. _____

Energy and environments

In the following passage, the words in bold have got mixed up. Rewrite the passage on another sheet of paper, with the words in the right places.

The Sun gives us two kinds of energy: one is **food** and the other is **grow**. Green **light** change the Sun's energy into **heat** by a process called **photographs**. We use the first part of this word when we talk about the **photosynthesis** made by a camera. It is a Greek word for **healthy**. The second part of the word also comes from Greek, and means **plants**. When an animal eats green plants, it uses the energy to **light** and be **making**.

Use the table below to sort this collection of living things into three groups, according to their usual environments.

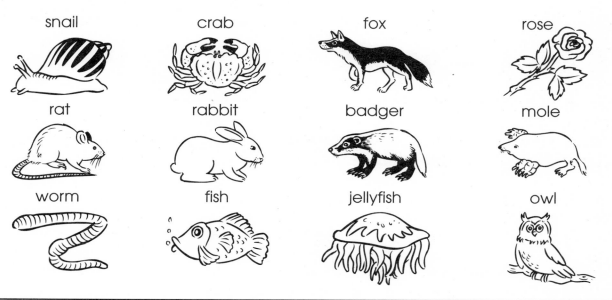

snail   crab   fox   rose

rat   rabbit   badger   mole

worm   fish   jellyfish   owl

Environment	Organisms
garden	
seashore	
forest	

For each of the three environments, write a **food chain** using some of the living things shown above. Write on another sheet of paper. You may have to add the names of other living things.

Parklife

Amber and Sian went with their classmates to a local park. There were many types of green plants in the park. During their visit they made drawings of leaves, but they found this difficult because there were so many different types.

Their teacher said, 'In science, what do we do when we have lots of data and information?'

'I know,' said Amber, 'we can make groups by sorting or classifying.'

'Excellent,' said the teacher. 'We'll start with flowering plants. There are two groups with different leaf patterns.'

He showed them this picture of a leaf in Group 1. Amber and Sian each wrote a description of it.

vein

Write your own description here.

Now they had to find out about the leaves in Group 2. They found this picture.

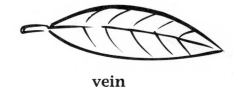

vein

Write your description of this leaf here.

Next to each leaf shown below, write 1 or 2 to show which group the leaf belongs to. Under each leaf, write the name of the plant it belongs to.

≫ S C H O L A S T I C   DEVELOPING SCIENCE LANGUAGE for Living Things 10–11